SISSY

SISSY

A NOVEL

BY BEN BOREK

BOILER HOUSE PRESS

For Natalia and Rufus

ONE

I write this from my floating second home,
My calm retreat when Vauxhall's sunny climes
Grow too hot-headed for my tender dome
(A vast cathedral full of golden chimes,
Which needs the river air to circulate
Throughout its sparkling naves, the placid weight

Of tidal-pull massaging from below
To let my fizzing cerebellum lull
Into a state where it is keen, but slow
And ready to compose). The gold-leaf hull
Now gently cuts the brown film of the Thames
And sprays a modest spindrift laced with gems

Of froth, which flicker, spectrum-like, to give
A billowing and nacreous effect
Encoded with the acronym ROYGBIV.
My *second* home, I wrote. You now suspect
I designate it thus to circumvent
A bill or two? But no. Our parliament

Has never seen my buttocks on its benches
(And if it ever did, the scarlet leather
Is where I'd sit, not in the squalid trenches
Of spin where any change in tabloid weather
Demands a shift in policy and speeches
As cloying as a plate of sugared leeches,

As tart as a carafe of puréed rind.)
So, no, my status is affirmed – your guide
Throughout this story, which shall soon unwind
For both of us – this is a real-time ride
Through disparate lives: a provident donation
From Calliope, I just take dictation.

I glide beneath the beams of Albert Bridge.
Adorned with blinking bulbs, they rise in two
Loose cones to form an undulating ridge
Of fairy light which fights the spreading blue –
A battle that the thousand fading eyes
Are doomed to lose against the waking skies

With Sisyphean, quotidian recurrence.
This crepuscule is sacrosanct to me,
When London's only effervescent currents
Are liquid and beneath me, when I'm free
To let my narrative, unbothered, rove
Through increments of indigo and mauve.

Soon I'll be dressed and up about the growling
Of rush-hour traffic (human and mechanical):
My duties as your scribe require some prowling
Around protagonists in scenes botanical
And urban, multicultural and plural,
Homogenous and more remotely rural.

But surreptitiously surveilling targets
Will only work once one has prey to prey on –
No use a choral work in many argots
If there's no burnished podium to play on.
So I must thank the muse for this bequest
Of characters. She promises they'll test

My wits and your credulity, but life
Is, as she says, more strange than any whimsy
A poet may dream up. His blunted knife
Cuts narrative from fabric which is flimsy
And has its sectile stitching fraying wild,
Forever being tweaked and reconciled

With what is his internal truth, that numinous
And frangible kaleidoscope of *Ars
Poetica*, his alternately luminous
And tenebrous conception of the stars.
My planetarium will be the world;
I'll let the constellations be unfurled!

Now, day's deep marbled eye has opened wide
And settles resolutely overhead
To fix a stare upon the riverside:
Ghanaian cleaners stumbling home to bed;
A walker with his melancholic dog;
Three matching tracksuits on a languid jog.

So I'll moor up here, under Vauxhall Cross,
And take the stairs to where a bus is bending
Beneath the solar-panelled terminus
Whose leaning roof now glimmers bright, distending
At sixty sharp degrees – a giant gun
To threaten the admonitory sun.

In Canto One, when he began Don Juan
(Began, but sadly left the thing unfinished),
Lord Byron sought a hero. Not a new one –
He thought the very term had been diminished
By such a dim profusion of contenders –
The tabloids soon exposed them as pretenders.

Oh, "plus ça change," you say, "how cheap is fame!"
The quarter of an hour, that great Warholian
Presentiment now seems a distant flame,
A relic best housed deep in the Ashmolean –
Now fifteen *seconds* is the current span
Of most celebrity, then all eyes pan

Rapaciously away with clicking mice
To see who next has fallen from a taxi,
Whose diet now is Goji juice and rice,
Whose new tattoo describes mount Cotopaxi
Erupting up their backs in plumes of ink
Or who can't seem to drive without a drink.

So Byron pinned his hopes on Juan, listing
The many he'd rejected as too gauche.
(Two stanzas full of heroes, some existing
In ruddy flesh and some, like Desaix, Hoche
Or Clootz, he felt, despite their gallant stature,
Had rather awkward foreign nomenclature.)

But I have no such choice. I have my orders
To start my tale, I may not state a preference.
I have precise coordinates – the borders
Of Lewisham and Southwark, the grid reference:
G6, p.105 (my *A to Z*
Lives photographically within my head).

The muse informs me she is well aware
Of all the current modern nonsense riding
The media's congested thoroughfare.
She says she has no interest in providing
Sensation for the sake of the sensational.
And that her "freakish" tale is "progestational..."

"A poet mustn't overlook this donnée
That you've been graciously bestowed by fate.
A vintner offers you a rich Chardonnay
Or Baune, perhaps a Volnay'98,
And you reject it? No, you sniff and swill it,
Then drink! Your one concern is not to spill it."

(This is the note she left me. I'd dispute
The vintage – '92 was slightly fuller
And more pronounced – but still, I found it cute
That she had made the effort.) "Your ampulla,"
(She goes on) "swells with an exotic range.
The fruit are novel, varied, rich and strange."

And I am pleased to hear it! And intrigued,
As I approach my first heroic personage.
My spinning legs are tired, my calves fatigued,
I'd welcome now a friendly inn or parsonage –
I'm cycling, as I must, to skip the hell
Of ever patronising TFL,

But navigating through the concrete vines
Of Renaults, Nissans, off-white vans, wide trucks
And buses lurching forth in serried lines
(The grid compressed then, in a manic flux,
Expanding to allow a bike to squeeze
Between a chink, before it entropies.)

Brings with it its own hazards of the flesh
And spirit, and (important too) the cloth.
My suit, clean on this morning, smelt as fresh
As spring dew. Now a cloying, pungent broth
Of perspiration permeates my trunk
And I can taste my own damp, sultry funk.

No matter. It's the lesser of two Hades –
The 436, a mobile public manger,
A nematodal, crimson-clad Mercedes,
Contains far worse aromas, and more danger
Within its hot articulated husk,
So I endure my own secreted musk.

I overtake the bus and fill my lungs
With blissful schadenfreude and bilious vapours
And leave its population's many tongues
To chatter in their seats and read their papers
In Farsi, Hebrew, Mandarin and Slovak
Behind my pedalling feet and engine blowback.

I pass the six-pronged Doric portico
And yellowed copula on St Mark's blunt
And looming hulk – the hue of dirty snow
Compared with Oval station's burnished front –
And cycle down the New Road, Camberwell,
Towards the south, against the traffic's swell.

I have to speed up. My benignant muse
Has given me a brief I must obey.
I shoot through lights, mount pavements, disabuse
Schoolkids and postmen of their right of way,
Down Rye Lane, Peckham, past the opening
Primark, ZA Afro-Foods and Burger King.

At Peckham Rye, I cut across and take
A verdant breath and think of seraphim
Revealing in angelic tones to Blake
An epiphanic light across the scrim
Of dew-jewelled Common from their lofty perches
In glowing sycamores and silver birches.

I cannot pause too long for an aubade
Upon this hallowed patch. The night's ablution
Of moonlight drains away, the avant-garde
Of chirping birds pronounce the dissolution
Of mystic, lunar energy across
South London's quickly fading milky gloss.

And I have reached my target, like a missile
Propelled with pure afflatus I have sought
The heat of my adventure's source, its fissile
And fertile core of energy clenched taught
Within a weirdly latent ball, which I
Must now explode before my reader's eye.

The muse has been as generous as any
Philanthropist – one with the softest spot
For storytelling and pronounced antennae
For scouting out a convoluted plot.
Her taste is ornamental, Romanesque;
The arches colourful, the vaults grotesque.

Perhaps I should explain? I'm now in place –
Imagine me an insect on the wall –
My usual, neatly bearded human face
Transmogrified beneath a furry caul,
My periwinkle suit now camouflaged
In cornflower wallpaper. With eyes enlarged

Like mirrored domes projecting greenish flashes –
Obsidian kaleidoscopes, unflinching
Within two fiery rings of barbled lashes
(Which serve as useful grappling hooks for pinching
A grip of picture-rail or windowsill) –
I stare and take my slow, delighted fill

And creep along the Woodchip on six feet
To settle on the doorframe of the bedroom.
The door is strangely wide – a square oak sheet,
Its ample breadth is equal to its headroom.
And through it, as my eye continues creeping,
I see a mammoth bed, and someone sleeping.

Can it be someone, rather than some *two*?
And here the muse's ribbon is untied,
The shiny paper scatters right on cue
As person one, a woman with hips wide
Enough for three casts off the heavy quilt
(Pilled, patterned like a Stewart tartan kilt).

She's naked, and we see her bulbous form:
A lozenge, diamond, hourglass in reverse,
Her arms and legs all fit *one* body's norm,
Her face suggests a fortysomething nurse –
Her slim and handsome jaw and cheeks, her nape
Furred blonde and lightly freckled – but her shape

Between her distal tropics (north of nipples
And south of thighs) is of another order:
Flesh corpulently bulging forth in ripples
Of chiaroscuro stretch-marks which marauder
With variegated fervour like dry dunes
Across her middle section's plump balloons.

She shifts an inch and sixty inches shake.
The bed heaves mournfully, the floorboards screech
With high-pitched strain, but, no, she doesn't wake.
Like breathy mermaids singing each to each
Her adenoidal nostrils alternate
To fill, then empty out her sleeping weight...

On second glance, I should say sleeping *freight*:
I now leap up and, spinning, copter-wise,
Outstretch my sticky wingtips and gyrate
Towards a landing pad of blotchy thighs.
Now fast, before she stirs and tries to squat
Me dead, I delve towards her central slot.

It seems that width is now a running theme
Within this ground floor flat – the massive entrance;
The bed ripped from a Brobdingnagian dream;
The sleeper Pantagruel's fat-swathed dimensions;
So it should come as no immense surprise
That I now face a gap of equal size.

My reading of the female apparatus
Is wide, and I've researched a great variety –
Some parking meter slots, some flaccid craters,
Distributed at random through society –
But this is not an orifice like any
I've seen and, as I say, I've clicked through many.

I feel as if I'm on a giant stage
Inside an auditorium's bright hall,
The curtains swish like crimson saxifrage
Caught up within a biorhythmic squall,
And as they part with each belaboured huff
Of diaphragm, backstage begins to slough

Its darkness and faint drops of man-made light
Sluice through. Now I perceive a thoroughfare
And, mindful of the muse I mustn't slight
By turning back, I wade through coils of hair,
Pass through the damply velvet aperture
And scramble to the dim, internal shore.

Lit languidly within, a bedside lamp
In fleshy tones illuminates the scene:
The chamber's ceiling, varicose and damp
Reflects the glow like breathing damascene
And heaves a little, like an inverse sea
Above a bed that bobs quiescently.

And there, asleep – a full-size, adult human
(Our hero, or at least one of a number)
Is curled up in moist quarters like a crewman
Inside a sticky hull. His foetal slumber
Breaks with his mobile's tintinnabulation
And spasms of concomitant vibration.

My view is now through scores of shaking lenses
As our true hero, groggily recumbent,
Shifts upright in his narrow bed. He cleanses
His sticky eyelids of the crust incumbent
Around each canthus like two pools of curd
And finds the phone, now that his sight's less blurred.

He shuts it off and sheds his duvet cover
(A map of Europe, faded after scores
Of boiling washes, and which we now discover
Was printed when the hefty ferrous doors
Were bolted across Mitteleurope's spine
And wars were cold). It's twenty-five to nine!

He's late for work. He stumbles to a hole
(I follow at wing's length) and with horrific
Abandon, eructates with all his soul
(This action loud and vilely vaporific).
Then, sliding through his mother's willing girth,
He executes a daily, clumsy birth.

"Nations unborn your mighty names shall sound"
Is well enough, but men, at thirty-four?
There's little latent triumph to be found
In finally processing through the door
Most humans manage, even if stillborn,
To pass through once and there remain... still born.

With this in mind I give my apologia
For my choice of our hero's name. To run
Each night back to the safe maternal loggia,
To re-become the same unrisen bun
In mother's oven every single night:
His name *can't* bask in an heroic light.

So Sissy we shall call him, not too meanly.
Chochotte sounds rather biscuit-like, *Waschlappen*,
Too wet and painful, resonates obscenely,
Maminsynek would too directly sharpen
His negatives, *Korkak* would fit the need – as
Long as you all were fluent Turkish readers.

Milksop might do, but... too late, I've decided.
It's not too cruel, arcane, or else abstruse.
It doesn't mean the boy should be derided,
And I shall talk it over with the muse –
She wouldn't like too dull (John, Bernard, Chrissy)
Or outré (Wolf), but should be fine with Sissy.

We've now skipped forward and in medias res,
On overpopulated, densely seething
Macadam, morning holds her passion plays
Replete with fuzzied lines and shallow breathing.
The sun has finished its reluctant rise
And each commuter mourns the night's demise.

We'll gloss over much of the ugly jostle,
The *my seat, your seat, may-I-pass-by-s, sneezes*,
The Oyster-bleep that fuses to colossal
And constant tinny pitch when each bus seizes
With human weight and seneschal and vizier
Slop in to flee the Underground' yet busier

More brutal forms of elbow war, canned air
And whipped heat round the escalator's tubers.
It's almost more for me than I can bear,
I feel the final bars of MissaLuba's
Sanctus, its chorus shrill, its rising drumming,
Best fit this scene: there's peace but something humming

BEN BOREK

Beneath the surface, primed to roar and rear up
And break society's fragile meniscus
Of hard-won politesse. I think I'll gear up
For any conflagration, use my viscous
Toe-tips and whirring back-blades to decamp
To ceiling height and spare the backseat cramp.

From this blissful though slight remove I watch him,
Our knight at arms, sit bleary-eyed and ailed
By myriad dull gripes – birthmarks that blotch him
In scarlet up and down his hairless, scaled
White vertebrae and peek above his scarf
To make his nape an autodiograph,

And boborygmic gut that here presages
The need for his habitual pre-work session
Within the office throne room (he engages
The same end cubicle's modest discretion
Each morning at precisely 08:06
Where, simultaneously, he de-sticks

His flopping fringe from unctuous, cliff-face flat
And pimpled forehead – this endeavour aided
By glass-paned cabin doors)… enough of that,
However, as we've not even paraded
Along the Walworth Road or even reached
Camberwell Green, where buses loiter, beached

By waves of idiotic regulation,
Which make them wait, doors open, chill intruding,
The decks convulsed in nauseous, bored vibration,
While drivers wait on signals from colluding
Officials clad in hi-vis orange livery
Who regulate Performance and Delivery.

As we approach this holding cell for rusting
Leviathans he fights a further ailment –
This one more socio-spatial though: the gusting
Of voices from both flanks. Their swift curtailment
Would salve the mutual eardrums of the flock
Of work-bound souls but seemingly a lock

Is stapled across each disgruntled face
In classic English fashion so they brook
The double foghorns, stomach the disgrace
(And crook a barely shown, yet heartfelt snook)
At having to be audience to chatter
Of such *prostacki* (loutish) subject matter.✦

Now semi-withered with exasperation
Our Sissy bites down on his nether lip
And concentrates his gaze on the formation
Of rain-wet rivulets that swell and drip
Like tiny cataracts along the panes
Of greasy Perspex, spreading like grey veins

✦ (I'll have to censor for the sakes of any
   Who, like myself, feel *żółciowy* (splenetic),
   Whose stomachs gurgle bilious (*schorowany*)
   When forcefully exposed to such frenetic
   Displays of public passive-aggressivity
   iPhones transmit with 4G conductivity).

   Forgive me these few foreign terms invading
   My narrative; I can't control the spout
   From which my muddled lexicon's cascading.
   Sometimes I suffer such linguistic drought
   That when the stopper's loosed a thankful gush
   Of words pour in a multilingual rush.

Before they fall and prick the sweating brows
Of passengers with window seats. The aisle,
It seems, despite discomfort, still allows
Fare-paying inmates travel without trial
By water (though knees roughly bruised will amply
Make up for chugging forth to work undamply).

The bus-shake oscillating through his bones,
He shrouds his head inside the *London Lite*
And checks the Nikkei 225, Dow Jones
And FTSE, reads synopses of last night
On television, lets his bleary eyes meet
Susannah's (sporting "glamour from the high street"

On page 16) then breathes a wheezy sigh
(His favoured, almost default, exhalation)
When in the corner of his blinking eye
The rust-and-cream tiled front of Borough station
Slips into view to signify his flight
From the accursed 40 is in sight.

As he descends, half tripping on to Tarmac,
We catch a fleeting portrait in the bus's
Waxed flank: pale blue eyes, pupils wide and tar black,
His nose a Russian sailor's, eyebrows trusses
Of auburn fur that somehow lash together
His face and keep it whole in breezy weather.

His haircut an unruly Velcro helmet,
His Burton suit too large across the back
But with its arms too short, each one a pelmet
Of wool to help conceal his sorry lack
Of lengthiness throughout the limb department,
He strides as if he's braving an escarpment

Despite the fact that London Bridge's camber
Is relatively soft. This grim traverse
In which he joins the bank-bound, suited mamba
Of fellow travellers who then disperse,
Flow up the hill and down King William Street
All fixing their dead eyes before their feet

I call the Wasteland Walk. (I'm just relieved
I didn't have to plod this route myself
But rode on Sissy's shoulder as he weaved
Through bodies widening like a coastal shelf
Of steely businesslike determination
Until he reached his (my, our) destination.

Before he knows it, blinkered, automatic,
He's at his desk: The hum of hard-drives waking,
The muted whine of traffic, the pneumatic
Purr of the air-conditioning all making
A sanitised and corporate reveille,
Conducive to a profitable day.

What does he do? At ten it's a collation
Of business strategies, a seminar
(Initiatives for Data Renovation)
At twelve, then lunch at Sirin's Coffee Bar
With Ben, the man who manages the lines –
At least that's what his job title defines.

Their morning in particular we'll deal with.
It's here that, after all, our tale commences.
As Ben and Sissy sit the Gaggias squeal with
Frothed milk and air that rapidly condenses
And settles upon surfaces just like a
Thin layer of dew on fields of green Formica.

The conversation turns and leaves behind
Such topics as the broken finance server
And takes this tack: Ben says: "Why don't you find
Yourself a woman, Siss? You do deserve a
Contented and fulfilled romantic life
As much as any man. Just take my wife

And me as an example – if I lost
My job and had to queue at the Jobcentre
In Peckham, it'd be a meagre cost
Compared with the loss of my dear Magenta.
A woman wholes your half – I know, it's corny...
But anyway, Sissy, you must get horny?"

"Don't get me wrong. I don't expect a wedding
Tomorrow. Whirlwind loves are just in books.
Your lack of action, though – it does my head in!
OK, enough! I'll stop. I know it looks
Like I'm obsessed, but, listen, I'm your mate."
Through all this, Sissy scans his empty plate.

This theme's not new; Ben gets inversely heated
In rapt proportion to the cold reserve
His colleague manifests. Inertly seated
Before him, Sissy never deigns to swerve
From diffidence and shrugs of sad evasion –
A concrete wall to Ben's suspect persuasion.

Why must our hero always be resistant?
Why does he clam so tightly up when love
Becomes the theme? His complex is consistent
With his domestic set-up (see above):
His residence within his mother's womb
Has stunted all potential as a groom.

It has, as you'd imagine, been a thorn
(More like a javelin) in Sissy's side.
Effectively to never have been born
Has been a weighty skeleton to hide.
The impact has been manifold and anguished:
When classmates all had sleepovers he languished,

Compelled by some deep-seated urge each night
To take, in the most literal of manners,
The station of the foetus. Fears the sight
Of his abnormal bedroom would throw spanners
The size of asteroids into the works of
His friendships with Dan Green and Johnny Berkhoff

Meant he dissembled, thought up wild excuses
Or else told blatant lies (when not avertable).
He'd cry himself to sleep amid the juices
Of Mother's insides. An incontrovertible
Deep knowledge grew within him that he wouldn't
Feel so safe elsewhere, ever... he just couldn't.

Coition is, of course, absurdly awkward
When, instead of bridal chamber, hacienda,
Stained mattress, cheap motel room, beach, heath, orchard,
Two grown adults must slide through the pudenda
Of a third, contort, undress, and touch each other
With tender happy strokes – this while the mother

Is witness – in a sense – if not with eyes,
Then through her sense-impressions, from the kicks
And prodding she sustains, from all the cries
Of pleasure (or discomfort) that she picks
Up aurally as well as through vibrations
Caused by these passionate cohabitations.

BEN BOREK

A history, then, of conquests and seduction
Is not what Sissy boasts of – no Don Juan,
Our hero, though this versified production
Will hopefully provide him with a new one!
(In short, he's innocent as Adam, when it all
Comes down to contact best described as genital).

At 19:27 he heads home
Past Lloyds's chrome exoskeleton, St Paul's
And its bluff often-scaffolded sick dome
(Now ringed by pigeons whose insistent calls
Seem somehow to drown out the lurching cars
And buses and the hubbub from the bars).

He takes a little detour and sits down,
Observing the Tate Modern and the river,
And, realising now he's formed a frown,
As deep as it's intractable, a shiver
Runs through him. He reacts with odd despair
And shudders in the warm spring evening air.

It seems the earlier barracking from Ben
Has hit him harder than he thought it had.
"It wasn't just light banter between men,"
Reflects Sissy. "Ben really thinks I'm mad...
What is it with me? Why am I so odd?
I almost wish I had a faith in god..."

But seeing as he doesn't, he just gazes
Into the dimming heavens and he heaves
Another weighty sigh. The clouds form mazes,
He fancies, through his gloom, and he perceives
In this a sort of spiritual significance:
To solve them all would lead to great munificence!

Now up, up, past Chalk Farm and Camden Town,
We'll leave the umber river way behind,
Past Belsize Park... that's good, now slow right down,
And slower... stop! In Cricklewood you'll find
An Eastern household fond of vodka, E,
Noam Chomsky, Goldfrapp, Echinacea tea,

The liberation of the guinea pig,
The "subject as a process", not a state.
(One free from labels such as Tory/Whig,
Male/female, Marxist/NeoCon, post/late,
State/nation, nation/state.) You want their names?
Those barely-burning arbitrary flames

That signify so little, that this house
Would rather do away with (but they must,
For ease of social movement, never douse
And scatter into nominative dust).
"I have to call you something," reasons Wassily,
Calm in the face of Izabela, sassily

Renouncing Iz or Bella, Belle or Iza,
On grounds of child abuse – she had no choice.
This cognomen was thrust upon her, she's a
Mute victim of her parents' whims, her voice
Was not fully linguistic when a baby.
(This infant state though, she's inclined to, maybe,

See as a blessing these days, as more "real" –
Outside symbolic orders, all those boundaries
That curse all conscious people.) Here a deal,
Albeit short-lived, strikes inside the foundries
Of Wassily and "Izabela's" thinking –
Communication by a means of blinking!

Three blinks – "hello"; one blink preceded by
A (left-eye) wink – "what time is it?"; eleven
Alternate flaps (begun with the right eye) –
"I read an early monograph by Bevan";
One blink, right eyebrow raised, left eyebrow static
(That's difficult!) translates as an emphatic

Communication of reflexive doubt…
They're interrupted. Words, the very things
That Izabela's so het up about,
Drift (violently, she feels) in from the wings
(The wings in this case should be read as "kitchen")
As audible now – Jan and Magda bitching:

"The 'Risk Society'" (Magda makes rabbit-
Ear speech-marks round the phrase with fingers stained
With terracotta gloss – she's in the habit
Of decorating monthly) "means we're chained
By half a dozen scientists' opinions –
Confirmed by all their bureaucratic minions!"

"All those of us who take the risks don't know'em
And those of them who know the risks don't take'em..."
"Point taken, but we're talking, so to show 'em
To proles like us is not taboo! To make'em
Accessible to our empowered sphere
Is where the challenge lies... is that all clear?"

These two continue rattling round semantically
And Slavoj Žižek's name keeps being quoted
By Magda (and by Jan as well, but frantically,
To emphasise a flaw, some notion floated
That he feels should be shot down like a Zeppelin
For being far too smug, full of encephalin

But lacking in stuff cardiac and humanist)
And Magda in her spattered smock and cardigan
Keeps rising to this baiting, starts to fume, a mist
Of heartfelt rage enshrouds her and, to calm again,
She storms back to her roller trays and turps
And curses "pseudo intellectual twerps".

The gesture passed from Wassily to Iza
Is easily predicted – eyeballs roll
Up into bony sockets "*Boże*! She's a
Touch incandescent these days! Like her soul
Has been molested roughly in her sleep...
Best leave her to *pędzel* (brush), she'll keep

Her scathing front up till she's found a fella,
Some sense of what she's here for". "Don't get woolly!"
Admonishes the solemn Izabela,
"You seem to think existence isn't fully
Osiągnął (realised) unless you double
And reconfirm yourself in love's mad bubble –

That tenuous, lugubrious delusion!
That *faiblesse* of the intellectual fibre!"
(You'll note, Dear Friends, to circumvent confusion,
To make the sense-exchange a little lither,
They quickly gave up blinking like mute birds
And fell back into Iza's dreaded words).

"That's not what you said earlier today!"
Says Wassily, "When I prepared, then carried,
Your toast and *citryn* tea upon a tray
Upstairs to you in bed." (These two are married,
Dear Reader, and there's no risk of a break-up.
They only row like this so they can make up.)

An odd couple,✒ they made their Warsaw pact
When Wassily was on a term's exchange
From Minsk to covertly examine tract
And tome and document beneath the range
Of Lukashenko's slick-haired, gurning goons
Who thought him there to study "Slavic Runes".

✒ Legends of Gdańsk uprisings had inspired him.
Wałęsa's walrus strength, fierce resolution
And matching *whale-horse* facial hair had fired him
With thoughts of shipyards sparking revolution
By rousing restive kin to risk a beat-down:
A strike to put collective Polish feet down...

Warsaw, twenty years on, though, disappointed –
That *Solidarność* spirit had long faded.
He saw instead bright skyscrapers anointed
With multinational motifs that paraded
The message: *There is cash here for the few.*
The rest can clean the streets in the EU.

That fire, lit seven years ago, still smoulders.
Their feet still tangle sweetly on their futon.
Wassily still compiles his angry folders
That prove how Belarus is dissolute. On
A manic basis Iza hits the gym
And runs back home to make demands of him.

———————

One night, morose, he fled a fractious meeting
Of counter-system misfits and got drunk
To save himself from taking in the bleating
That billowed round in circles till it sunk
In bogs of argument. With cold kebab
For pillow, he slumped on a paving slab.

He thought of Belarus and how to leave it.
How, even in a freer-speaking nation,
It's cash-the-knife takes history's joint to cleave it
Wide open, complicates with oil-taxation,
The animosities of gas-supply
Or strong-arm Putin fingers in the pie.

A girl with flailing mane and tar-black eyes
Cut through his reverie. "You look depressed.
Perhaps you'd like a liquorice surprise?"
"A what?" "A cigarette. Rolled on my breast
With these" (she waved her fingers, flashed red tips).
A smile spread over Wassily's cold lips.

He watched her dirty hands carve through the smoke –
A butterfly, a riot, a field of wheat,
A pair of mating swans, a smutty joke,
A grey, anonymous, rain-dappled street,
A dacha in the steppe-land brightly painted,
And then no more... dazed Wassily had fainted.

BEN BOREK

Thrice nightly, half of Cricklewood unleashes
And vast collective groan and stuffs its ears.
The terraces all shake, untethered quiches
Self-detonate, bowls crack, as Iza nears
An otherworldly climax so ecstatic
That Magda shares it upstairs in her attic.

———————

He woke up some time later (well, he'd had to,
As time will only move in one direction –
Straightforward and determined), slightly sad to –
His dreaming had inspired a taught erection
Through vivid episodes, lifelike and laden
With images of last night's dusky maiden.

Where was he? In a bed, in an apartment,
Żelazna Street, within the erstwhile walls
Of Warsaw's ghetto, South Wola Department,
A room with crumbling, Cheddar-yellow walls
(Thus stained by years of diligent release
Of liquorice by whoever held the lease).

He wanted, more than anything, to pull off
His soggy bedclothes and to find between
His body and the bedside table (full of
Art-quarterlies) his dreaming's lucid queen.
"Don't hog the *kołdra* (duvet), kindly share!"
Squeaked up from underneath a pile of hair.

(He'd thought it was a pillow but now rheum
Cleared from his crusty eyes like clouds dispersing
Post some myopic blizzard and the room
Took on its daylit form). The dry unpursing
Of lips whence the familiar voice had spoken
Confirmed he had a bed-mate, and she'd woken.

Let's pull the *kołdra* off ourselves and peek,
Dear Readers! Let's draw back and view the tableau:
Two bodies, rather pallid, one more sleek
And one more hirsute, coiled up in a rouleau
Of limbs and eiderdown and feral strands
Of jet-black hair and newly-curious hands.

It's here I'll fade the retrospective camera
And leave this scene of lovers' introductions
("I'm Wassily." "I'm Iza.") Let them hammer a
New naked two-part harmony. The ructions
Of this impulsive pact are still withstood
Years later (i.e., now) in Cricklewood.

But, one last thing, before we leave the past,
Before this scene of nascent love is shaded
To subtle grey to brown to then, at last,
A tactful blackout where their shapes are faded
Into the lens's pupil... for a trifle
Please humour me, take one last gleeful eye-full:

Their feet! Hers long, unpampered yet unweathered,
The tendon from the calf protruding neatly,
A residue of sawdust; his wide, leathered
By years of barefoot football, dark, discreetly
Encased in charming sprouts of flaxen hairs –
A sumptuous pair of overlapping pairs!

Enough of Slavic orgasms. Let's follow
Poor Sissy as he gets back home to Dulwich.
We know by now that he's inclined to wallow
In *Lac Ennui*. No change tonight. A dull itch
Has fixed itself determinedly to
His loveless status and what he should do

About it as he's bundled from the bus
By girls who smell of bubblegum and hormones.
He trots up mum's cracked paving, stops to fuss
Deep into various pockets at the door, groans
And jets a loud exasperated breeze
Out of his nostrils: Sissy's lost his keys.

Consider Sissy's will to be a camel,
And every minor aggravation: straw.
The tears that he's been trying hard to dam all
His journey home now flood as, at the door,
He slumps and sobs and feels a warm release:
At times it's only weeping that brings peace.

41

BEN BOREK

This sudden fit of tearful self-deflation
Reminds one of a Rabbi at the wall.
He's nodding, heaving, every emanation
More pliant, more a maudlin, dying fall.
He bashes at the door in his abandon.
The door knob's what he finally lays his hand on.

His knocking interrupts the tom-tom roll
And all-too well-known coda that decries
The climax of EastEnders (Martin stole
The takings from The Vic, but this stash lies
In tatters and he hasn't even spent it
On Stacey's backstreet surgery, he's lent it

To Peggy's Godson Chris who's gone and blown it
On contraband Armani, which is now
Submerged in Thames-muck – Chris's mates have thrown it
Off Walford Bridge, to pay him back for how
He rigged the sweepstake at the annual gathering
Of postmen's widows... sorry, I've been blathering,

A pointless thread, the Poles would call *bez sensu*,
The French would call *enervant* and the vicious
Would call something unpleasant I've no bent to
Despoil these pages with in case it fissures
Your sense of calm enjoyment or decorum...)
And anyway, just look who's at the door: "Mum!"

Cries Sissy through wet veils of snot and tears.
"Oh, heartsweet!" she replies and turns to guide
Her crying man-child home before the jeers
Of schoolgirls rise like an unfriendly tide
And cause a further dent in Sissy's mettle.
"Oh come to kitchen. I put on my kettle"

She's standing in the kitchen in her curlers
But in a nervous fret she pulls them out.
Her silken floss of hair starts to unfurl as
She drops them to the floor and pulls a pout
That doesn't here reflect a hot flirtation
But more a deep, maternal consternation.

He's curled up in the kitchen on the lino
And desperate to attain his homely spot
Back up inside but mum's not game. "Look, I know
You have disgusting day... please tell me what
You so set up about before you crawl up.
Look, here's Earl Grey, my heartsweet, drink him all up...

And Sissy, wipe you *nos*! You dropping lumps
Of gunk on lovely suit." Left hand on hips
(Fanned-out and oversized like waist-bound humps)
She grabs some Kleenex and adroitly strips
The man-size for her man-cub of their sheath
Of plastic with her stubby yellow teeth.

There's now a brief hiatus: Sissy's brittle
And raw proboscis gushes like he's just
Pulled out a stopper. Pretty soon there's little
That isn't touched and glazed by this wild gust
Of liquid, semi-sinuous and thick.
The kitchen's like a beach in nasal-slick.🪶

🪶 Myself, I can't abide the waste of paper,
The messiness of Kleenex and their ilk.
When stuffily congested I just drape a
Well-laundered handkerchief of Persian silk
Across my swollen organ of olfaction
And blow out in one measured, manful action.

Now plump, unstately Sissy roused his bulk
And pulled his quivered sinews from the sticky,
Off-beige and scarlet chequered floor. "Don't sulk.
Please, heartsweet, try your later daddy's trick. He
Would visualise shit *ejfor* paper and
Great fountain pen, then using spectral hand✑

✑Mum thinks this *melon-drama* must be "putative".
(She mixes adjectives because she's too
Ambitious with her English. These commutative
Attempts at sounding erudite are due
To making reasoned, but in fact fallacious,
Connections between words like "great" and "gracious"

And "putative" to her somehow connotes
A sense of constant battering – its tenuous
False-partner: "pugilistic" (she's heard quotes
From Lennox Lewis.) Sharp, though disingenuous,
She made her odd conflation. Please excuse her.
She's trying very hard to slowly lose her

Slavonic template wherefrom every word
Is dragged and dusted down and then translated
Internally at speed before she's heard
To utter in the tongue of her belated,
Ambivalent yet laissez-faire new Heimat.
She misses Lublin's food, but not the climate.

Mum struggles most of all with words like particle.
She wants to stress the tic and not the part
And really is dumfounded by the article
(Poles, Russians, Czechs, Serbs, Croats never start
A sentence with an "a" or "the" or "an"
And say things like "I'm writer" or "he's man").

He write most up-pent thoughts and firmly blocked
Reflections, all exclosures pride suppressed.
Once psychic ink dry dad discovered locked
Bi-way from heart to tongue was loose. Expressed
In speaking form to me or to nice counsellor,
They halfed in gravity. He felt more bouncier."

So son then told his mother of his woes,
Of how his chat with Ben that working day
Had made him feel abnormal, but he chose
His Blackberry's bright LCD display
To represent his thoughts in pixel form.
He typed, then spoke, then wept another storm.

At all this sobbing, mum✦ felt less inclined
To implement a "tough love" course of action
And let him go to bed as usual. Blind
Without her spectacles (dropped in reaction
To seeing Sissy keening in distress)
She'd felt him clamber up inside her dress.

✦ So, how did mother end up here in Britain?
I'll paint her route in adjectives: circuitous,
Malodorous, romantic, clumsy, smitten,
Slow, picaresque, heartbroken, lost, fortuitous.
And now some nouns for colour: PRL,
A pregnancy (the babe conceived in Hel),

A fiancé, connections (ticket West),
A meat-truck, rag-and-bone cart, crate of gin,
Three weeks shared with smoked herring in a chest,
A painful break-up leaving East Berlin,
Etc. the rest is rather sketchy –
You ask her of the past and she gets tetchy.

Her reasoning had been uniquely rational
(For her). Briefly, two twos had equalled four,
She saw her son's attachment as irrational –
At once perceived the fundamental flaw:
The routine to which he was most addicted
In fact just left him more and more afflicted!

Now Sissy sits within the sticky mess
That constitutes his living room inside
Another living being – I confess
The paradox is odd. Once he had cried
Another soup-bowl's worth of pent-up woe
He'd felt his natural rhythms start to tow.

———————

But Sissy had a father for a while.
They didn't share a gene or even culture.
His name was Brigadier. He'd never smile
But somehow, for this while, before the vulture
Of mortal time (embodied by a stroke)
Swooped down for him, he'd been a decent bloke:

He'd found a home in Peckham, got a flat
Eventually (the council queue was longer
Than all of Proust). And goodwill then begat
Goodwill and he resolved to be a stronger,
More grateful man than when he'd first arrived
From dusty Lagos and he'd ducked and dived.

I don't speak ill of diving or of ducking.
I've had to do my fair share in my years.
North Peckham's not the place to try your luck in
If you're a little wet behind the ears...
And in the Brigadier's case he was sopping.
He really couldn't manage more than shopping

His domicile has many novel fixtures:
A desk lamp made of steel (an Anglepoise);
The desk itself of streaky oak; three pictures
Of Morrissey; a clutch of office toys
(A mini snooker table, mini cues
And mini balls he's anxious not to lose);

A metronomic, chrome-balled, tick-tock frame
That serves no useful purpose whatsoever,
And toy Kalashnikov that shoots a flame
For lighting one's cigars, though smoking's never
Been entertained "indoors" since once, three years ago,
He fell asleep and rendered mother's ears aglow.

For spinach, Guinness, curry, chips and tea.
He dodged the crackheads hustling round the green
At Camberwell (they'd start with 50p
For some fictitious urgent phone call ("Been
Completely stranded, Guv, I've got to call
My mum, she's old, she's dying... is that all

You've got there..? Hang on, let me see your phone...
And now your watch... and look, some notes! Don't talk.
You lied! You're minted, Guv. Leave me alone.
It's my phone now. My watch, my money. Walk!")
The Brigadier was not too apprehensive –
He never carried anything expensive.)

He'd got some menial work (all cash-in-hand)
Refilling white dispensers full of soap,
Cheap one-ply toilet roll I understand
To have the rough consistency of rope,
And when his short-term stint near Bank was over
His boss said: "Want some full-time work in Dover?"

He opens up his iBook with a click
So smooth and ergonomic it provides
A minor sensual flutter. Pretty quick
He is online – his modem cable slides
Out through mum's midriff like a plastic sprout she
Maintains most patiently; a dangling "outie".

A wireless network wouldn't penetrate
Through human walls and, though they both endeavoured,
The process left mum feeling rather faint:
The on-screen message: "net connection severed."
So Ethernet from desk, through flesh, to wall
Was deemed the most commodious to all.

His remit there was thus: transport the skips
Piled high with burger cartons and used Mates
To Ramsgate landfill sites, disgorge the ships
Of slops and sewage, cart it on to crates.
And there, performing one last stinking tow-away,
He met his pregnant, blue-lipped Polish stowaway.

Domestic "bliss" would last just seven years,
But two-thousand five-hundred homely days.
They found the Dulwich house. The Brigadier's
Was sold off by the council in a craze
Of private equity and hedge fund dealings
Which rather hurt the local tenants' feelings.

————————————

There were indeed dark whisperings of bribery,
All tied-up with the Lottery, the minister
For "culture" and the funding of the library.
(It's thought that Sega wanted to administer
A bookless library and they picked their place
And time – the MP bought it with good grace.

Amid the purpled cheeks and sideways looks
She cut the ribbon, blessed the library open:
"How good to see a library with no books!"
No sooner had this *scripted* speech been spoken
Than all the money men in suits at Sega
Raised crystal glasses to their witless saviour!)

He has a more expansive second life.
And so, logged-in, he's now transmogrified.
Divorce proceedings with his second wife
Have meant he's let his other interests slide.
So now he concentrates on dealing meth-
Amphetamine and Ketamine with Beth

(His soon-to-be third jelly-bosomed bride
In less than half a year). Why not move fast?
His blunt ontology: "Once I have tried
It's pretty soon the hour to switch and cast
Them off (but stash their stashes) and then choose
Another babe with fancier tattoos."

The line of work selected for this cipher,
Requires a line in brutal little beatings.
His second wife, Charmaine, he'd had to knife her.
She'd got a little jealous of his meetings
With Bethany at parties where perversions
Extreme and variform were the diversions.

His name is Neno Brown. He's six foot nine,
(Instead of a more modest five foot one).
The product of meticulous design
With graphic tools and torso-sculpting gun.
Accompanied at all times by his rubious-
Eyed Doberman (dimensionally quite dubious)

Named Boss, and acolytes Jeb, Ham, and Daniel,
He'll find a meek, loquacious Jeff from Florida
And fleece him (Boss will fleece his sorry spaniel)
Then implement the next phase – things get horrider.
Dear Readers, if you're sensitive please skim
The next few lines until they're done with him.

In six months he's established quite a gang
(Ice T would here refer to Neno's "set")
Who operate with venomous, cold *sang*.
These confrères in delinquency were met
In Second Earth's bad neighbourhood, Old Hoxton.
His bloodlust and bald hate had awed and shocked them.

And round his haunts, Old Old Street, Breeze-Block Lane,
The Spittle-Fields, Arkangel tube, Queen's Cross,
He swaggers, dealing virtual pills and pain
To any virtual prey he comes across.
An über macho front that doesn't fit
With timid waking truth, you'll all admit...

A merchant needs a market. Neno Brown,
A businessman, requires a constant stream
Of dribbling, suppurating folk in town,
Like mangey cats flocked round a bowl of cream,
In desperate drooling want of all his wares,
All sporting desperate, yellow-lidded stares.

"Demand" for Neno best translates as "need"
And with pronounced and blunt amoral greediness
He gives poor Jeff's thin cobalt veins a feed
Of merchandise to thus encourage neediness.
The troika – Daniel, Jeb and Ham – all help him
By pinioning poor Jeff, who's shocked and yelping.

So, this, his gruesome *modus operandi*
Could rather turn one's stomach. You should hold
The notion that it's all a feat of hand-eye
Co-ordination on a twelve-inch, gold-
And aluminium-plated, backlit screen,
Or else endure your innards turning green.

An instant customer, now Jeff will visit
The office Neno rents in Breeze Block Lane,
He'll brave its rough façade to find exquisite
Gold chandeliers, plush armchairs, meekly crane
His sweating brow round Neno's foot-thick door
And intimate that he would like some more.

And there, reclining louchely like a parody-
Amalgam of a dozen arch Bond villains
(He's on a chaise-longue) Neno watches cowardly,
Wan, shivering Jeff (a ringer for MacMillan
In '63, when stressed out by Profumo)
Who sidesteps Neno's bodyguarding Sumo

(The Yokazuna template from Street Fighter II
With added weapons and a bleach-blond wig)
And cowers. "Oh dear, Jeff. You're not quite right, are you?
Perhaps you'll let me offer you a swig
Of calming and restorative white wine?
It's past the sell-by date, but should be fine."

Here Neno Brown loves to act the charmer,
The louche sophisticate with well-bred airs.
The theory goes – the more the crook's a smarmer
The more his fall-guy's taken unawares
When suddenly he snaps and twists the knife –
But really, this is filmic stuff. Real life

Is brutal from the start when you're with gangsters.
They don't have time for sweet-talk when they're working.
They quickly deal with smart-arses and pranksters
Or anyone whose face protects a lurking
Amusement in proceedings – here a blunted
Domestic tool will leave the grinning stunted.

You get the picture, though: Jeff makes obeisance
At Neno's knee and sniffles on his lap
Then finds himself an armchair (faux-renaissance)
Once he's paid up. He starts wildly to tap
His forearm till his antebrachial vein
Is plump and pulsing fast beneath the strain.

The joint is jumping back in Cricklewood
(Quite literally, one puff, then pass it round).
A house party to celebrate the good
Reviews that Magda's had – her "gnostic sound
And digital amalgam installation"
Was praised on Art.com for innovation:

A sublimated neo-modern pose
Dissecting history and linear time...
Concerns itself with how core-borders close
And tangle in the liminal sublime...
When selfhood is itself here reassessed
As a communal question, as a test

Of sculptural vocabulary and
Of how well one can tap into the fears
Of fashionable, despairing pseudo fin-
De-siècle attitudes for our post-years,
Post-time and post-societal conjunction
Of meta-sexual thought and moral function...

The artspeak staggers me as much as you
And really I should offer a translation:
She took a pot of fishy-smelling glue,
Some clippings from a monthly publication
Moj Pies (My Dog), some fibre-optic cable
A mirror, slide projector, Bruegel's *Babel*

In reproduction, printed on some sheet,
A massive mirror ("art must be reflexive!"
The mantra Magda's often heard to bleat),
Then with a strict and earnest art-invective
She filmed herself filming herself as she
Installed the installation that would be

The film itself – its content was the stuff
She then discarded like an unfit mother.
(Although for Magda it was quite enough
To put it all in boxes, and not smother
Her embryonic child-art with a cloth
Or muffler or to boil it down for broth.

In fact she found the objects a vitrine,
In case one day she had a change of heart
Or someone from the *Zeitgeist* magazine
Suggested she reprise her plastic art
By means of deep regression to the bricks
Of substance that her filmwork now depicts.)

At such occasions there is always talk
That veers towards the arch and plain hubristic:
"I find the way you've used the sealing caulk
To *ac-tu-al-ly insulate* artistic!
Few artists these days have the vim or gumption
To use things for their own intended function!"

"I like the fact you like my home repairs,
But, truth be told, I had to seal the shower..."
"Of course! Of course! That's just what no-one dares
To say these days!" We join them at an hour
When all this talking's rather petered out –
The soporific Belarussian stout

Must take the blame – and, Readers, don't you find
Some variants of beverage do plunge
One into verbose realms that, rarely mined,
Result in quick-fire talk, but, like a sponge,
Somehow soak up the chatter till a juncture
When all speech bubbles get a common puncture?

Though here's a stalwart bunch who, of the crowd
Who came and filled each smoky cubic yard
Of dining room and kitchen with their loud
And multilingual banter, still seem hard
At work, with undiminished appetite,
Consuming wine and talk right through the night:

There's Wassily, of course, sat on a plinth
Of plywood by the kitchen sink (which drips)
And Iza next to him, a squelchy synth
And drum machine their soundtrack as she sips
Her apple juice and vodka from a flute
Which should by rights be filled with *Dom* or *Brut*.

Their mutual body language here exhibits
Tired discontent – they'd rather be asleep
But, a) feel friendly duty still inhibits
Their bedward flight and, b) they want to keep
Their kitchenware in one, exclusive set
And don't trust these odd guests they've never met:

A painter from Dubrovnik, earnest, bald,
His pate-stubble deployed in concentrations
Which, if you'd squint a little, could be called
"Hirsute schematics of dark constellations"
(As Iza does, behind a shielding palm,
To Wassily, who glories in her charm).

There's Monika from Prague, wrapped up in chintz
Upon the lap of Richard from West Ongar.
She doesn't seem to heed his plaintive hints
That they could leave together and prolong the
Festivities elsewhere, he knows a bar
That opens late, and then, he's got a car...

The painter drums the lacquered table's edge,
The legs of which are stacks of pilfered bricks,
His eyebrow (singular) a mobile hedge
Of pubic hair, his eyes two rheumy slicks;
He's swallowing as if he's in a drought
Which means he'll soon let something thoughtful out.

He turns to Magda, "Tell me, if you'd deign
To let me, in a manner, keenly shine
A lamp into the potholes of your brain
And find, beyond the cranial fence, a shrine
To thought on future creativity..."
"You mean, what will my next big project be?"

Magda completes his question for the sake
Of all of us. "Well, Sasha," (that's his name,
The painter with the layer of downy flake
Across his neck) "I thought I'd play a game
With archetypes." "I *see*," he says. (Not seeing
Too much but oozing lust from all his being.)

"Shall I explain?" asks Magda, stiffly crossing
Her legs away from Sasha with a swift
And sonorous abrasion of her stockings
That cuts a high-pitched nylon-scented rift
Through Sasha's spine. "I think it's time I tried
To be a proper, decent, Russian bride!"

At this the painter turns a pinker shade
Of pink than strawberry bubblegum, and swoons.
He thinks "Oh joy! Arrangements must be made!"
Imagines languid autumn afternoons
Spent semi-dressed discussing Creed or Giotto
With Magda in his well-heeled Crouch End grotto.

This bubble bursts as quickly as it's blown
And Sasha's rosy reverie (and face)
Turn ashen white, his fantasy is thrown
Asunder. Now he's wishing up a space
Beneath him – one that he could tumble down
To hit a lake in which he'd gladly drown.

"I know, I know, it's terribly *vesély*
(Hilarious) of course," here Magda's chuckle,
Which ripples outward from her modest belly
Like waves upon a sea of lace and buckle,
Just reinforces Sasha's disappointment
And has him thinking up some late appointment

He mustn't miss ("but no, that would be lying"),
So there our maudlin painter sits and chokes
His throbbing pride. To camouflage his crying
He pokes his face into his neighbour's smoke
To make his eyes more watery and red
And tilts his quivering psoriatic head.

BEN BOREK

Then Magda starts her sermon, still amused
At her own proposition: "Marriage? Me?
Ha! Signing up to freely be abused?
To be a trope in mass misogyny!
To shuffle my own person through the door
Marked 'virgin/cleaner/goddess/mother/whore!'

This project is intended to critique
The very Russian gendered bifurcation
That has its women painted, pliant, meek
(But beautiful), imbued with desperation
To please its venal, macho, ugly-looking,
Male populace with selfless love and cooking."

Wassily, all his sleepiness dispelled
By all this fired-up talk, his pink ears pricked
By any enterprise that seems to meld
An anti-bullying, *nouveau-Russki* shtick
With muscular, productive, thinking art,
Enquires into the artiste's project's heart:

"What is it, then, exactly, that you plan
To execute? Just how will your polemic
Against unreconstructed Soviet man,
His frosty, heartless blanket of endemic
Faux-leather jackets, shaven heads, *big oil*,
Be brought to some elucidating boil?"

At this, Magda contorts her compact face –
In truth it's rather squashed but not unhandsome,
An overactive facial marketplace
Where nose and eyes are held in bullied ransom
By all the manic advertising chatter
Her tongue spills with its raucous, hawking patter:

"It's not so much the Russian men directly,
But more the consequence of this milieu
And how the western world will circumspectly
Go grazing on the female *esprit doux:*
Just picture all those Englishmen who squirm
Afront their keyboards grooming girls from Perm!

I'll use a sawn-off shotgun of invective
And target *all* the men I find to blame
Then issue them a sobering corrective.
Here I intend to take another name
And new 'location' and to masquerade –
I'll be the sunny, model, Russian maid!"

"Aha, I get it, but…" "Yes?" "Well, it's just…"
"I'm listening…" "Well, once you've done your posing
And lured, or teased, with mugshots of your bust,
And sent your quarry messages disclosing
Your deep sincerity, your chaste demeanour,
The fact that you're a gifted cook and cleaner,

And once you've also charmingly suggested
That portly men don't constitute a turn-off;
That grey, receding hair, when unmolested
By Just For Men, is sexy; that to burn off
A middle-aged and Grolsch-inspired spread
One should be, most effectively, in bed.

This last point should be subtle though, of course.
You'll have to tread a very fragile line.
On one hand Sir will like this bit of sauce,
But on the other, surely he'd refine
His search if you seem loose or dissolute,
And find a much more wholesome brand of cute.

But anyway, you weave your clever snare
Of coquetry and innocence, what then?
You have your glut of brutes in underwear
Slumped over keyboards. How to get these men,
Their monobrows and stubbled triple chins,
To suffer for their hegemonic sins?"

"So tell me, have you seen the movie *Seven*,
With Brad Pitt's wife's head in a cardboard box?
Of course you have. I aim to swiftly leaven
The gender-biased loaf, to flush the pox
Of all of the aforementioned machismo
By holding up a mirror with *this* gizmo!"

She wields her mini-GoPro cam and gloats.
Now Wassily is worried. Has he heard her
Correctly? Does she want to slit the throats
Of lonely cyber-bachelors? To murder
A man a day for one bloodthirsty week?
He hopes this reference is tongue in cheek.

"Oh Wassily! Not literally, don't worry!
But I find quite ironically appealing
The notion of reflecting all these sorry
Reductive, dull desires... I'll bounce the feeling
Right back at them tenfold, in triple speed:
So, for the glutton, I'll embody greed

And for the lustful, well, that guy won't *sleep!*
For Sir with complexes more Viennese
I'll dress up as his mum and let him weep
Into my starchy bosom, or to please
The wrathful I'll conspire at every turn
To let the touch-paper of discord burn!"

But Wassily is not entirely wowed
As much as all the rest. (Magda has mounted
The table, blown wet kisses, giggled, bowed
Amid much cheering – which, in truth, amounted
To Richard, Monika, the painter Sasha
And Izabela wrapped up like a pasha

In pseudo Arafat.) He thinks it's all
A little too exploitative and wishes
That somehow Magda could draw up the gall
To properly attack the bigger fishes.
But no artist will meet his dream to usher
A second wave of *glasnost* in White Russia.

Magda's announcement forms the natural apex
Of what has dragged into a long conclusion
Of party-time. She jumps down like an ibex
And bangs the painter's head (ouch! a contusion
Of streaky blues and purples will mature
And leave him even more morose – and sore).

The crowd disperses languidly, all kissing
The politic five times on soggy lips
But drunkenness ensures a lot of missing
And spittle either stains the stubbled tips
Of chins and studded noses, or it's sent
Into the air to glaze the firmament.

The maudlin painter, nursing throbbing bruising
Of spirit and of cranium, departs
With Richard, whose blunt, ineffectual schmoozing
Of Monika has petered out. Their hearts
Are heavy – one romantically destroyed,
The other more priapically annoyed.

Magda and Izabela traipse upstairs
To do that feminine party-going thing
Of visiting the ladies' room in pairs
And Monika, once she's seen Richard sling
His jacket (and poor Sasha) through the door
Of his Sierra, curls up on the floor.

This leaves just Wassily. He drains the cans
And bottles through the sink's ceramic sluice,
Divides them for recycling's sake, trepans
A gaunt, discarded grapefruit for its juice.
He gulps this down, winds up the waning clocks,
Turns off the fairy lights and checks the locks.

My gaze is drawing outward, eyes are red
With tiredness and all the tar-filled smoke.
I watch as Wassily trots up to bed
And, now retreating, snuff the urge to stroke
Dear Monika's plump tootsies which have poked
Invitingly outrneeaasuuugh (sorry, nearly choked!)

It's not a crime. I shan't apologise
For loving pedal pulchritude: smooth arches
That angle from round heels to then surprise
With dactyls deftly ordered like proud larches
Atop a leather landscape! I could weep
For joy when watching toes drop off to sleep.

And haven't you too revelled in the swelling
Of ankle bones that bulge in lambent skin?
Or found yourself enthralled beyond all telling
By well-stuffed socks – what perfume lies within?
The notes that feet emit are rich as wine
From cellars stuffed with myrrh and eglantine.

No, not today. No more. I'm turning in.
My Krupnik's warm and ready. I can hear
The shipping forecast dreamily begin
("Gale warnings Forties, Viking, South Utsire").
I'm in my Hokusai *Great Wave* pyjamas
And need a rest from other people's dramas.

So, good night, sov gott, beaux rêves, dobranoc!
We'll reconvene upon the other shore
Of sleeps' warm sea (and of this page) for lots
Of toast and coffee and I'll tell you more
Of Sissy, Izabela, Magda's scheming
And Wassily's intense erotic dreaming.

Some of you might be worried now – but please,
I am a gentleman! I wouldn't grope
A pair of sleeping feet or brush the knees
Of somnolent and placid prey... I'd hope.
This is all voyeuristically exciting
But there it stops. My job here is the writing.

So many things to do! I've marinaded
Some corn-fed duck in Mexican molasses;
I've burnt some incense; gently I've abraded
My cuticles and toenails; oiled my glasses;
I've tenderly shampooed my hirsute breast
And forearms... as I soon expect a guest.

My private life is private. You can pry
With subtlety or rough interrogation,
As ardently as any DCI
In Sun Hill's bowels, or tempt an abrogation
Of willpower with bribes like sugared fruit
Or satin hose, but they will find me mute.

In coy demurral, inwardly I'll tut –
I do hate gossip and salacious tattle,
But I'll concede one fact before I shut
The door on this boudoir of giggling prattle:
At my express request my guest will be
In flimsy sandals, open-toed, size three.

And if I have to briskly force a closure
On my narration, end this chapter dead
Without a natural cut, keep your composure –
The doorbell will have turned my perfumed head
But I'll be back again. You'll keep abreast
Of everything, but sometimes I must rest.

Where's Sissy? That's the question you'll be asking
It's been a while since we watched him bed down
In warm, yet moist, content. He dropped off basking
In pseudo-potency as Neno Brown.
But now it's morning, Neno's not in sight,
And Sissy's had a restive, fretful night:

His dreams were a melange most disconcerting:
Wild scenes of Neno's wretched troika hooting,
Engaged in ritualistic bouts of hurting
A blameless *Second Earther*, calmly booting
The ribcage in without a human care
As some poor soul clawed after precious air;

Then, as the picture grew more sharp and taut
And centred its attention on the mound
Of kicked-in, bleeding humanoid, he caught
A petrifying glimpse of his two, round,
Inflated, scarlet cheeks, his tuber nose
And watched his own fat eyelids slowly close.

The dream time – not the kind that folk down under,
Indigenous to Uluru's rust red
And dusty vistas source for mystic plunder
(Oneiric timecode in a sleeping head)
Skipped forward to a tableau: woman, park,
A gravel path, young pine trees, trilling lark.

She has his mother's gait, though it's less lumbering
Than usual, and her waist is girlish-thin:
There's no internal freight, no load encumbering
Her youthful locomotion from within.
Her features are arranged in glowing proof
Of happiness and optimistic youth.

The dream contains an otherworldly feeling,
A sort of heavy mist of honeyed joy,
The sunlight, smells and colours hum, revealing
A pulsing phrase to Sissy's brain: "My Boy,
My Boy, My Little Boy" wafts through the trees
And Sissy's mother trembles at the knees.

The Skies grow biblical with charcoal *stratus*
And *altocumulus lenticularis*
The dream-mood shifts its synaesthetic status
And things get weird (a bit like in *Solaris*✒
When Kelvin sees his dear departed wife,
A revenant, now full of spectral life).

✒A little pedagogical digression,
  If you'll permit. It adds suspense as well.
  It's pedantry, I know, but here's a lesson
  In Polish elocution: You can tell
  The way to stress these names by reading them
  In English metrics, thus: Stan-*is*-ław Lem

  Well done! You've got the stresses. That's much better!
  Please note the line discreetly running through
  The ł's proud trunk and that the final letter
  Is not in fact an English double "u".
  The ł equates to "w", the English phonic,
  So ław is "wav" (the "w" here is Teutonic).

The growling heavens then bespeak tarnation,
The birch trees wriggle gaunt and twisted boles
And Sissy's mother's younger incarnation
Stands helpless as the ground beneath her soles
Starts creaking, then it ruptures. Now the grass
Resembles more a sheet of cracking glass.

A host of dark, malignant little creatures
Pours out from every fissure, nook and cavity.
They all have Sissy's podgy, sweat-glazed features,
But here they're morphed and mangled with depravity:
"My Boy. My Little Boy!" they all reprise
In mockery of Sissy's mother's cries.

And, while we're on this subject, there's a slip-up
That pains me like an arrow in the thorax:
Imagine how I groan and curl my lip up
When one young friend asks: "Have you read Ben Borak's
First novel?" and my blood seethes hydrochloric
When friend two says: "I thought you said it Boric."

Untie a simple "knot" inside your mind
By stripping brittle consonants away.
That leaves my first vowel bare. Now quick, let's find
Some clothes for it, some vocal lingerie
To hide its open, slack-jawed nudity;
So please enunciate a forthright B

Then follow through, please part your lips. Controlling
Your flaccid English tongue, now tap its wick
Against your palate to produce a rolling
Yet delicate, swift "Rr", then let it flick
Back down to nestle on your lower deck
And end with a decapitated "neck".

This scene is now aflame; a wild Gehenna
Of beasts whose cries unite in one shrill whine.
Their bodies are like squirrels', downed sienna
And auburn, but their tails are serpentine
And muscularly thick. They swarm and smother
The abject, shrinking shape of Sissy's mother.

Now Sissy wakes, of course perspiring, coughing.
His sweat is like iced water and his chest
Is tremulous and judders as if sloughing
A poisoned skin, as if he's just confessed
To something wicked. Inwardly his scream
Runs through his nerves to cauterise the dream. ♪

He glides through morning clumsily, still haunted.
He spurns tea, smoothie, Special K and showering.
He braves the number 12, today undaunted
By schoolgirls' jibes. The alcoholic glowering
In Elephant and Castle's subway maze
Can't penetrate his troubled, vacant daze.

♪ Vladimir Vladimirovich Nabokov
Disdained books that served up an easy moral
Almost as much as he thought Freud a crock of
Unpleasant, musty fairy tales. His quarrel
With simple verdicts gleaned from simple dreaming
Chock-full of lazy symbols got him screaming:

"Whoever has these dreams? *I've* never had one!"
He called Freud "the witch doctor of Vienna"
And quack (and evidently quite a bad one)
Whose readings lent a banalising tenor
Of medieval sex 'n' death to all
Imaginative acts staged since The Fall.

He surfaces a little once at lunch
In Sirin's, which is empty save for Ben's
Broad grin. They both have plates of *Credit Crunch*
(Red cheese, fried toast, two eggs from Southwark hens)
And both drink tap water of fierce acidity
(A squeeze of lime) that Sirin's calls *Liquidity*.

They sit in silence – Ben because he's grinding
The chargrilled toast and leathery *faux Brie*
Between his teeth, but Sissy's clearly finding
No interest in his food. He seems to see
No point in it and hasn't touched a bite
But stares inertly at his *London Lite*.

His listless gaze lights on his horoscope.
Despite himself he stirs a little. *Taurus*,
He reads, *your natural aptitude for hope*
Should not be stifled. Do not be so porous
And malleable. You have a harmful tendency
To smothering yourself with your dependency.

The coming weeks are cosmically propitious
Your ruler Venus moves into a trine
With Virgo – most romantically auspicious
But also quite disruptive. You must mine
All your resources and enact a change –
A long-desired target's now in range.

Your luck will be most strongly manifest
In chance connexion with the numbers 9
And 40, letters B and S divest
Felicity, the East is most benign,
The colour purple (not the book, the hue)
Shines brilliantly opportune for you.

Look out especially for an exotic
Incursion in your life, a foreign chance
Is on the cards, look out for semiotic
Suggestions in each daily circumstance.
(For further revelations on your sign
Please call this premium-rate prediction line...)

Ben pauses from his rapid mastication
And pulls a pose he thinks to be parental,
Or like a doctor, pre-examination,
To reassure the treatment will be gentle,
His empathetic, veiny nostrils flare
Like two dark potholes lined with bristling hair.

"Oh dear. There's something pressing on your mind?
It's not the forecast for the second quarter?
I know that Sales and Broking are behind
By thousands more than us, so if the slaughter
Of one or two unfortunate young lambs
Is unavoidable, I'd call *us* rams!

Not funny? No. Okay, I know, bad metaphor.
Or was it more a simile? I'll verify
Tonight when I get home. I must be better or
It won't be long before I go and terrify
Magenta with a term she thought she'd learnt
In class and leave her faith in teaching burnt."

At this, a purple reference, Sissy raises
An eyebrow, pops a square of blackened bread
Into his downturned mouth. His friend appraises
This appetite as progress. "As I said,"
Adds Ben, now dribbling egg-mulch on his collar,
"Magenta is a very gifted scholar."

"You mean she isn't English?" "Nope." "Nor Scotch?"
"Not Scottish." "From the States? Vermont? New York?"
"No, none of them!" Ben fidgets with his crotch
And flicks off fallen debris with his fork.
Oh poor Magenta. Next time that I meet her
I'll try not to be such a messy eater.

"She's not Canadian? From Winnipeg?
Or Manitoba?" "Nope." Ben's now applying
A cloth to ketchup stains across his leg
Which could be gunshot wounds. "Go on. Keep trying."
"I give up guessing, Ben. I think you'd better
Just tell me where she's from and how you met her."

The duo walks and talks, at Ben's suggestion.
He finds a brisk ten minutes after eating
Dispels the need for naps and aids digestion.
He now delineates the fateful meeting,
Recalls the first coy emails that he sent her
How he transposed Marushka for Magenta.

"It has a youthful ring to it. I felt
Marushka sounded like the kind of name
You'd give a gran with skin like walrus pelt.
Magenta's like a swaying purple flame,
A candle with a dripping waist, a thorn
Whose cut is sweet, a cello in the dawn."

He says that signing up with Slavic Beauties
Was, quote, "the best investment of my life"
And Ben has major City trading duties
So that's no modest claim. "I met my wife
In person, in the tender flesh, god bless her,
Last year, at Hotel Lubov in Odessa.

I recommend you try them. Apropos
Of what I said before, you know, some action,
It couldn't hurt to give those guys a go."
Ben fears the same belligerent reaction
He had last time they spoke of this and braces
Himself for one of Sissy's gurning faces.

But Sissy thinks "A semiotic sign!"
His star chart is still ringing in his ears.
There seems to be a threaded mystic line
That weaves itself through everything he hears –
The foreignness! The 40 (yes, his bus –
A touch tendentious, sure, but still a plus).

That sparkling S for Slavic, B for Beauty,
The *foreignness* of all of this! He trusts
"Exotic" didn't really mean Djibouti,
Or Casablanca's souks and pungent gusts
Of shishas, nor the toxicating swell
Of incense sticks (he can't abide the smell).

(Of course these sketches are a flighty notion
In Sissy's head: he's never really ventured
Across the channel, let alone an ocean.
His home life leaves him literally indentured,
Though in his childhood mum and Brigadier
Once spent a week with him by Brighton Pier).

He's sure the "East" from Phylemon the Mystic,
The gifted sage employed by *London Lite,*
Referred to wintry lands once Communistic
And anyway, he reasons, it's quite right
That this should be a territory aflood
With kismet – it's the wellspring of his blood.

Besides this unexpectedly quixotic,
Romantic strain of evidence, what clinches
In Sissy's eyes is not this new exotic
Yet atavistic sense. The thing that pinches
A muscle in his face and sets aflutter
His lips and eyelids in a silent stutter

Is Phylemon the Mystic's last, chromatic
And mildly patronising divination.
For Sissy, what is most profoundly vatic
Is Ben's long elegiac illumination
Of all the qualities that he has lent her
By christening his wife afresh Magenta!

So, flushed with new afflatus for proaction,
Our hero reconciles to log right on
As long as he's not driven to distraction
Upon the bus and all his verve is gone
Before he gets back home and can ingress
"Upstairs" between the pleats of mother's dress.

I'm sorry, pause one second while I steal
A little glance. I'm not a curtain-twitcher
In normal circumstances but my zeal,
Now pregnantly expectant for a picture
In Kodachrome, 3D, and five feet tall
Has let my usual well-checked standards fall.

Alas, not yet though. All I can distinguish:
Three pudgy pigeons gorged on lamb passanda,
A Turk and Serb at war in Pidgin English
Beside the former's steaming Fiat Panda,
Its innards spilled like shrapnel. Oily scars
Point out the latter's buckled handlebars.

My sympathies, of course, are with the cyclist.
I've made my point before about the grime
The evil car emits. I'd gladly blacklist
That Turk for armed assault. His violent crime
Does not use spears or hot-irons for searing
But metal shells equipped with power steering.

For now, I'll have to wait for that as well –
The day when every car-wielder is banished
To haunt a ring of automotive hell
And every car is summarily vanished
Into the mouths of crushers, and then spewed
Like metal cud to make tin cans for food.

Let's end this talk of waiting and distract
Ourselves from this disquiet of the heart
(And flesh. Well, Reader, mine, at least, is wracked
With anxious pimples as if something tart
And bitterly exciting has been loosed
Throughout my limbs to leave them feeling goosed).

He's made it home unbothered and unscathed
(The bus was oddly calm. Is it half term?),
Perfunctorily acknowledged mum, changed, bathed
In *Adidas Sport Gel* (the tangled perm
Of hair between his legs and its locale
Got most attention in his rationale),

Excused himself ("I'm smashed to smithereens")
And slipped himself into his private space
(This took a while, as mum was wearing jeans).
We join him here in front his interface
With Slavic Beauties: *Log in now to meet a
Young, beautiful Tatiana or Nikita*!

He Browses, eyes and belly not in sync –
An old mistake,⟡ and one that now obtains.
As Sissy clicks from link to lustrous link.
Each keenly opened pop-up box contains
Another girl in grinning, supple poses
On spotlit divans strewn with paper roses,

Or dressed for bathing, polka-dotted, tanned
Precariously balanced on spike-heels
Upon a beach of pale synthetic sand
(Imagine now their coquetry and squeals
On hearing some lewd bark from out of shot
Instructing them to "pout more!" and "look hot!").

He soon constructs a long inventory
Of favourites – Dasha's bulging, sequinned chest;
Svetlana half submerged in Azov Sea;
Galina's lustrous hair – a wanton nest
Of frenzied curls and silver dickie-bows;
Upon a mossy rock in Siren pose

⟡ Nabokov's *Skazka* (1926) –
A Nursery Tale in English – does possess
A bitter little moral. It depicts
A playfully laconic Deviless
Who tempts a timid Erwin with the offer
Of a blissful little harem. She will proffer

Whichever girls he spots around Berlin,
(Cavorting in a green park's warm oasis
With woolly pup; on fairground rides; within
A greasy bistro's beer-fumed fug – their faces
And outfits painted in a breathless rush
With gaudy strokes of an excited brush.)

Tatiana with her face towards the spray
In wet-look yet diaphanous bikini;
Irina, on a bright blue, cloudless day
Her painted fingers gripping a Martini
Upon a terracotta patio
That compliments her skin's deep peachy glow;

Or Inna curled up on a blotchy pelt
Of some fantastic leopard/tiger hybrid,
Her long, protruding legs encased in svelte,
Translucent stockings, each mascara'd eyelid
A dusky Triffid, casting brooding tines
That spread like darkly shaded laughter lines.

And many, many more. If I reprised
The list in full, I'd waste a pleasant hour
And, frankly, as I'm sure you've realised
I've more important plans. We needn't scour
The female population from Khmelnitsky
To Volgograd and Brest along with Sissy.

Once one is picked a clever sign is seen,
He'll know that they have joined his happy troupe –
Frau Monde, the Devil, swears they will convene
In one fantastic, giggling, eager group
On cushions and on rugs (just think, their *feet*!)
That night at number 13 Hoffman Street.

The tale, of course, does not end well. Frau Monde
Sets Erwin one numerical condition –
If broken, then her generous magic bond
Will break as well. To claim his coalition
United to perform his act of god
He has to guarantee their number's odd.

What must be known: his eyes are avaricious
And keenly add a comely triple dozen
But his stomach is more anxious and suspicious
(As fear is bullishness's second cousin)
Between the eyes and gut – that's in his heart –
He feels he needs to make a cautious start.

The slender waists, the thigh-high boots, the stockings
All seem, although erotically beguiling,
A little *too* enticing, mildly shocking.
In theory they're near-perfect, but their smiling
Wide eyes and full red lips betray a lurking
Unnerving playfulness, a feline smirking

That Sissy thinks might be a bit full-on
For him, at least initially. He settles
His shortlist for this first brave push at one –
A berry-picking redhead, braving nettles
To fill a woven basket with dark fruit,
In rustic dress – less *sexy*, but more *cute*.

Midnight draws close, he heads for Hoffman Street
But somehow his collection's roundly even.
"Kein problem" – on his way he's bound to meet
A tired shop-girl or stocking-footed heathen
Before the clock sounds twelve enchanting peals.
And hark – a pair of brightly clicking heels!

He catches up with their attendant feet
And shapely back and silhouetted hat.
("She'll be my last, and best. A naughty treat,
The thirteenth girl. And then that will be that")
But then he sees her face and makes the stark
Act of recall – he'd picked her in the park.

He reads her introductory paragraph:
I on this site for hopefully to find
Mine future. Very much I love to laugh.
My character considerate and kind,
I like to walk on nature and to make
The tasty dishes, borscht and poppy cake.

I search the man which with me want to grow
The family. He must love animals
(I have one dog). I very love the snow
In winter and I'm loving dancing balls
(Prefer the Latin and the classic dances)
I love a candle dinner and romances.

I do not care the man is old or young
And not important also how his looks.
My future love have beauty like a sun
Which shine from in the soul. Like in the books
I will to become princess :) Now my heart
Await the mail from you, mine second part!

So Sissy quotes his credit card's credentials,
Creates a password and a username
But disregards the basic fundamentals
Of web security – they're both the same!
Now any soul with half a gram of nous
Could snoop around his private cyber house

So Erwin's left with nothing but a knot
That tightens in his throat. A limousine
Glows balefully in front the vacant lot
Where Villa number 13 should have been.
Frau Monde leans out, extends a chubby glove
Which Erwin gifts a kiss of thwarted love.

And rifle through the drawers of correspondence
Or, if they're more perniciously inclined,
They could unleash a form of written ordnance
And leave his *billets-doux* unkindly mined
With offers and suggestions of activities
Which don't exactly match his tame proclivities.

But what does Sissy write? He taps his Visa
Card thoughtfully against the iBook's rim
And ponders what to say, how best to please her,
And whether he should tick the box marked "slim"
Or "average", or if it would be right
To casually exaggerate his height.

But he can't focus, torn between his drafts
(Here I predict that there will be a number!)
And the grainy second jpeg: amber shafts
On distant lakes of dappled green and umber,
A few thin clouds that whirl and chase their tales
Above the rugged Balaklavan dales.

And in the foreground – this is where his gaze
Keeps avidly alighting – there she stands
Serenely still, her bright red hair ablaze
Against her pallid skin, her gentle hands
Are delicately clasped as if they hold
A cobweb spun from rare Crimean gold.

Lyudmila! (It's the only name befitting
A heroine of fair Slavonic stock)
In jpeg number three we see her sitting
Upon a shaded log. She twirls a lock
Of hair, a glowing filament of ginger,
Around her beckoning left middle finger.

She'll stay there beckoning into the future
As Sissy struggles with his composition –
He has in mind a cool yet stylish suture
Where form and message chime in apposition
As if they were stitched sheets of lyric tissue.
The trick, he thinks, is not to force the issue.

We'll leave him to it. I can hear the tapping
Of well-known toes arriving on my street...
They hit my path... and there's the forceful rapping
Of dainty knuckles on my door. How sweet!
She's not forgotten how to do the knock.
Just wait a second, I'll address the lock.

Oh gosh, I'm sorry that I had to vanish
In such a heady rush. I warned you, though.
But now my guest has left to meet her Spanish
Beautician in his council flat in Bow.
I am left to tiredly rearrange
My furniture and self. Our keen exchange

Has left the place, as always, slightly messy...
And left me drained and drowsy, but contented.
I'll clear away the edible confetti
And straighten out the clumsy rugs and dented,
Dishevelled mattress and within an hour
A limpid footprint exiting the shower

Will have dissolved and fluttered off to meet –
In some warm, carpeted backroom in heaven –
A host of other soft angelic feet.
I've put Debussy's *Nocturnes* on (it's Previn
Conducting an excited LSO)
And tidy with a satiated glow.

And while I do so, much as I would love
To recapitulate the last few hours
For you, dear Readers, that task is above
And way beyond my versifying powers.
Besides, I told you, I'm no gossipmonger
And anyway, I feel curious a hunger

For what is going on in Cricklewood.
Now Wassily is on the phone: "Allo?
Nyet? Nyet! Da? Khorasho!" ("No? No! Yes? Good!")
"Oleg! Oleg! Nie govoreet tak gromkó!"
("Oleg! Oleg! Don't speak so loudly!"). Hushed
And cautious he continues in his rushed

And rusty Russian for another minute
Whilst hunched over a notebook's yellowed face.
At intervals he jots a detail in it –
All dates, names and addresses have their place
In their own ink-drawn columns: his schemata
Looks like the artful score of a sonata.

Soon Izabela bumbles in, still groggy
And fills her king-size chrome espresso maker.
She's en route from the bathroom and leaves soggy,
Soap-scented palm and paw prints in her wake. Her
First impulse is to blearily assuage
Her cravings' fierce imperatives which rage

With throbbing resolution and don't leave her
Until she's had her coffee and her trio
Of Rothmans. Wassily drops the receiver
And shuts his battered book of staves *con brio.*
He needn't be concerned – at this benighted,
Ungodly hour, poor Iza's too short-sighted.

They have a brief yet venomous exchange –
Something to do with bedclothes and hot water –
Then Iza clatters round the cluttered range,
Pours out her babbling coffee with a snort. Her
Long bathrobe trails behind her as she stumbles
Back up to bed beneath a fog of grumbles.

Now Wassily, once he's completely sure
That he's been left in splendid isolation
Leans out a slippered foot, taps shut the door,
And redirects his eyes and concentration
Towards his cryptic list of scribbled data.
He jots down a quick note ("Gone out. Back later")

In magic marker, sticks it to the freezer,
Then calmly picks the phone back up and utters
"The Monument." He necks the dregs that Iza
Has left to simmer on the hob then scutters
Towards the door, pulls on his brogues and trilby
Then leaves – a Slavic, Cricklewood Kim Philby.

The sunlight comes in intermittent bursts
Through layers of moody north-west London cloud.
This piques, then cools, the early morning thirsts
Belonging to the bloodshot, scruffy crowd
Who gather underneath the jacaranda
In front the Beaten Dockets's pine veranda.

Wassily passes by with cautious haste
And feigns a foreign lack of comprehension
When met with an unlaundered, leather-faced
And under-dressed Glaswegian's coarse attention.
(Applying his most Slavic intonation,
He dodges all his pleas for a donation.)

Now wedged in – on his right a greasy pane
And backward view of Claremont Road retreating,
And on his left, an aural hurricane
Of ring-tones, rows and energetic eating –
Wassily cowers on the 189
Towards the Angel and the Northern Line.

A bright miscellany of human traffic
Alights and boards in various degrees
Of sanity and dress – the demographic:
Delinquent, Ashkenazi, Japanese.
In vigilant protection of his mission
He views them with discreet, but firm suspicion.

There's one man – tall, Caucasian, in a suit –
Who makes Wassily feel acutely wary:
Could he be in his villainous pursuit?
Observe him: handsome, sinisterly hairy –
His piebald beard befits a sinful crook,
He hides his spying eyes behind a book

With butterflies and moths across its covers
And has a generally malicious aura.
Wassily checks himself, breathes deep, recovers
His sense of cool and does his best to pour a
Diluting, lucid, level-headed quart
On top the coals of paranoiac thought.

Once off the bus and safely underground,
A calming isobar of starchy air
Shoots up the escalator and around
His stress-taut shoulder blades and dampened hair
(The trilby he'd removed near Hampstead Heath
To let some oxygen get underneath

And cool his sweat-caked follicles and crown).
The Angel's escalator – proud to be
The longest on the underground – creeps down
Its sixty-metre chute. Here Wassily
Has ample time to furtively undress
A Hoxtonista in a trendy mess

Of pseudo-rustic florals. His gaze roves her
Penumbral crannies and pellucid places.
He feels a little frisson, then reclothes her –
Sometimes he likes to linger just on faces –
She looks familiar – the sparkling nose-studs,
The *Joconde's* mouth, the cheeks like little rosebuds,

Remind him of his flatmate's, but instead
Of Magda's disarray of jet-black coils
This darling's hair is clean, paprika red
And vitalised with unguents and oils.
Wassily crooks an eyebrow, bites a lip –
Reflexive facial code for "get a grip".

He reaches pocketwards for his consignment
Of liquorice and fingers through the lint.
To concentrate his mind on his assignment
He has to *suck* something; a flattened mint
Will have to do for now, the Bassets packet
He now recalls is in his other jacket.

With menthol surging round his nervous system
He boards the Tube, selects an itchy chair,
Takes in strange faces without trying to twist them
Into demonic hoards with Gorgon hair.
The three stops breeze past: Old Street, Moorgate, Bank's
Glazed platforms where the pinstripe-suited ranks

All course out through the tunnels in a waft
Of fashionable fragrance-counter scents
From pungent creams to make the jowls soft
And body-sprays to fill the hirsute dents
Beneath the arms and spare all public noses
The bitter bouquet of *hyperhidrosis*.

While Wassily is busy formulating
Olfacto-social theses on "smell-class"
(With ostentatious fragrances equating
To flaunted bourgeois *objets petits a*)
The train slides out from Bank and its concomitant
Parfums and glides downhill towards the Monument.

Oleg awaits, as prearranged, before
That Doric pencil cut of Portland stone
Which rose up from the embers to redraw
The charred metropolis, to beef the bone
Of withered city skeleton afresh
With aspirant and monumental flesh.

A blue carnation (spray-paint: nature can't
Provide all the accoutrements required
To make the meeting foolproof) sits aslant
In his lapel. His Café Crème expired,
Oleg picks out his quarry's face despite
The lack of hat and reaches for a light.

Identified now by the cigarillo
Wassily grasps Oleg's free hand between
His two wet palms, slaloms the noxious billow
Of aromatic blue-brown smoke to lean
His humid cheek against his cool compatriot's –
This close embrace: reserved for fellow Patriots.

A little too conspicuous, this man-on-manism
Just round the corner from The City's eye?
Most broker-types prefer a Desperate Dan-ism
Of hetero-innuendo. Their Bovine Pie
Is lager, vindaloo, and self-awarded
Lump sums filched from old folk who they've defrauded.❜

Our duo of conspirators withdraw
From one another *under the brown fog*
Of Oleg's smoke and make towards the shore
Beneath the bridge, a ruddy, wrack-strewn bog
Which fills with more detritus when it hides
Beneath the oozing river at high tides.

Their spot is isolated, shielded, hidden
From onlookers by London Bridge itself –
A urinous and algae-dappled midden:
Above, the fulminating concrete shelf
Of roadway, and to either side blunt girders –
An ideal site for damp, alfresco murders.

❜ (A caveat, in case you burst your belly at
The generalised injustice of that verse:
The Square Mile did employ a certain Eliot.
The world would be less Modern, much the worse
If he had not done fieldwork for the Wasteland
Round here – although he hardly thought it Graceland:

I had not thought death had undone so many –
His verdict on the grey-clad, loping column
Of men on London Bridge. (More John than Jenny
Made pre-war mornings extra brown and solemn,
I'd venture...) and today one could remark it
Foresees our grimly flat-lined, hollow market.)

The water, in a fulvous lather, belches
Around the floor of desiccated brick.
Wassily moves, with succulent slow squelches
Of brogue in mud towards a patch of slick
Untrammelled lino (chess-board printed, glistening
In fast, refracted light) then says, "I'm listening."

Oleg, who up to now has walked in silence,
Now flicks apart his verbal valve. His speech
Is fast and sharp, an act of minor violence
On his vicinity. He spits out each
Raw sibilant and fricative with sickening
Élan, as if each vowel is soaked in Strychnine.

It's hard to make out each inchoate echo.
If one had a secreted Dictaphone
About the shore (say, *in a plastic gecko*)
One could play back the geminated drone
And aspirated nasals several times
Until one gleaned some reason from his rhymes.

"I have it. It is safe. You needn't fret.
The acquisition was, how shall I put it?
Not so straightforward. Everywhere a 'nyet'.
I overspent my fee. The difference, foot it
And then we have a deal. Cash for your Oleg?
Then I will tell about the man with no leg."

A muffled interval in the recording
As Wassily proffers a roll of notes.
Oleg collects them diffidently, fording
A damp network of foetid, shallow moats,
And counts them out in rapid, expert fashion –
An act of zealous lust and crude dispassion.

"Okay. All good. That is what we agreed.
But hidden costs? Please, ten percent on top."
"How *much*? Say two?" "Say eight?" "Don't make me bleed!
Say Five." Wassily prods a stiff full-stop
 Into the air and turns towards the river.
"And one more thing. I pay when you deliver."

The grainy dialogue tails off once more.
It sounds to all the world to me as if
Two hands are shaking on a soggy shore
(A dullish thud of palms, my anaglyph,
Which soon confirms itself as Oleg vents
A rasping "tak", which means that he assents.)

"So. I deliver. King's Knight to Pawn 4."
Wassily pauses, wary of a ruse,
Then cottons on and looks down at the floor.
"Assume you're playing white." He lifts his shoes
Across the lino in a careful gambit
Then, pulling up the tile, reveals a sandpit.

Inside, a wooden box. Inside the box
Another – like an oblong Russian Doll.
The fourth is bound in chains and safety locks.
"Oh dear. You're stumped?" chirps Oleg in his droll
Soprano. "I suppose you'd like the code?"
"Well, yes!" "It's Iain Sinclair's favourite road."

I now discern a puzzled scratching noise
As Wassily roves round his frazzled cranium
In search of the solution. His sweat cloys
Like lava carbonising Herculaneum
Until, resigned to drowning, cooked alive,
He cracks it, keys in "M" and "25".

The content is unpacked, unwrapped and placed
With delicacy on the strips of gauze
That had enshrouded it; the boot unlaced
And levered off with minimal rough force;
The seven toes confirmed. "Yes, that's the one!"
Breathes Wassily. "Now, here's your cash. Well done."

A harmony of mood imbues the soundtrack
With both men gratified to seal their deal.
Wassily's heart, as if it has been wound back
To normal speed, ticks on an even keel.
Oleg's is calmer too, now his cash nestles
Between his shirt and pulmonary vessels.

"So now you want the story, I suppose?"
Asks Oleg. "Yes. Well, no. Well, yes but no.
Now that we can relax, why not repose
In some place more salubrious? Let's go
And drink some Coke and frozen Wyborowa
Now that the grim formalities are over."

Oleg agrees – where vodka's intimated
One really needn't twist his brawny arm.
So, with the chessboard (evidence) cremated,
And Wassily's new foot now safe from harm
And packed up lovingly within its four
Containers, chains and locks, they leave the shore.

As they retreat, a yellow tugboat hums,
Tucked in behind a mottled iron pinion.
The handsome captain tosses bagel crumbs
Out to the circling gulls. In his opinion,
A plastic lizard is the perfect pet –
It never needs to eat or see a vet.

TWO

I have to check the blogosphere – from liberal
Conspiracies on oil and mind control,
To Fox News and its paranoiac dribble;
From Chinese voices smuggled out via Seoul
To musings arch and psychogeographic
On sex-drives influenced by one-way traffic.

And once I've read my fill I have my mail
To check, and a lagoon of spam to dredge:
From Lagos there are "dear friends" who regale
My inbox with a large financial pledge;
A dozen "manhood serums" also flash
Across the screen and offer "girth for cash!"

A little online shopping now as well.
A pair of satin Maison Margielas
In rusty gold – brogues "with a tale to tell"
As eBay seller Ben's descriptions tell us.
An oval toe, lined leather, inch-stacked heel:
€400 (plus the tax) – a steal...

Now I've completed these few morning chores,
It's time to check the Slavic Beauties site.
It's safe to say that Sissy bled his pores
Of all creative juice throughout the night
And as sleep wrapped his head in its mantilla
Of woolly black, he clicked "send" to Lyudmila.

He feels he has (he has!) made a great leap
Into an as-yet-undefined new realm
From off a ledge both comfortable and steep.
The thought nags that the newly airborne helm
Of his good ship is manned by some external,
Invisible and not wholly fraternal

Director, but he feels a heady mix
Of mockery at such a thought, and doubt,
And nervous resignation (such quick clicks
Of enter keys, like blurting something out
Or slipping daring notes beneath a door
We know a putative young paramour

Is on the other side of – perhaps pacing
The tiles in nothing but a damask blouse –
Are always followed by the thrilling racing
Of blood, aflutter, through the limbs that house
Its bubbling motion. There is no returning –
One's best off just indulging in the burning,

Like drops of scented wax on naked skin
Which, at first charring touch rejects the pain,
But with the sweet release of dopamine
Bids molten candle syrup fall again
Across a nipple, navel or whole torso
To replicate the thrill, but only more so).

Rebirthed again, washed, dressed, mum taken leave of,
The morning hell of public transport suffered
In stunted thrusts, with each belaboured heave of
The bus a small convulsion, he sat, buffered
Between two Maudsley out-patients – one twitching
In gay inanity, one fiercely itching

A point upon his tan prosthetic limb
(A "flesh-tone" matching pasty Anglo-Saxons
As poorly as Somalians like him).
The morning bus ride in makes Michael Jackson's
Most oddball picnics (face-masks, pink champagne
For kids and chimps) seem relatively sane.

Our hero disembarks on Borough High Street
And does the Wasteland Walk across the river.
Halfway across his heavy-lidded eyes meet
Another pair, bloodshot the hue of liver.
The head that they protrude from: Belarussian,
Blind drunk, and clearly suffering concussion.

This head stares on as Sissy swerves around it,
His scandalised proboscis stoppered tight
With scraps of sleeve. The odours that surround it
Are fungal and cloacal: they'd incite
A rush of retching analysts and hedge-
Fund managers towards the burnished ledge.

Starbucks, King William Street: a tired, anaemic
Barista in a regulation grin
(I think they're all drip-fed hyperglycaemic
Encouragement before their shifts begin).
She slaps steamed froth and syrup in a cup
And Sissy gets his glucose levels up.

He grows an instant white moustache while ambling
Down Cheapside in his usual disarray
Of pre-work fogginess. The slow unscrambling
Of Process and Procedures for the day
Spins round upon his mental carousel
On steeds named Sales, HR and Personnel.

Now at his block, a sub-de Meuron Ziggurat,
He huddles with a cloud of other smokers
And lights but barely puffs a low-tar cigarette
(He only smokes to pally up to brokers)
Then joins the queue to swipe his entry card
Redundantly before the sleeping guard.

His office greets him with its naked flare
Of halogens and daily brief strabismus
As every bureau, water cooler, chair
And tinselled cactus (residue of Christmas)
Spins with a ghostly twin until his vision
Adjusts and recombines its cell division.

Swine flu has set off superstitious waves
Of panic through the building as if Circe
Were lurking in the stockrooms or the knaves
And had the whole department at her mercy –
Perhaps she's spiked the juice in the canteen
With mythically protean poteen?

In consequence, as Sissy settles down
To gaze into the screensaver (a Titian:
Two cherubs, one with mirror, one with crown,
Attending to the haughty disposition
Of Venus wrapped in scarlet fur-trimmed robes,
A thumb-sized pearl in each one of her lobes)

The floor is lulled and empty – any cough
Now qualifies as hazardously septic
And gives one leave to take the fortnight off
And seek a pricey, liquid analeptic
Inside a gastropub in Billericay,
So half the company has pulled a sickie.

This calm suits our young suitor. With his fingers
Atremble he logs in and checks his mail,
Most thankful that his neighbour, Bob, malingers
At any chance (last week, a broken nail,
The week before, a pimple on his knee
Required a bed-bound week in Leigh-on-Sea).

And what now nestles on his virtual doormat?
A doctored gallery of "naked" actors,
A dozen phishing scams (including four that
I recognise – those charming benefactors
From Lagos), and some odd eBay receipts
That must be spam – unopened, he deletes.

These mails hold scant attention. Sissy's eyes
Flick up and down the re:'s and sent by columns
Like frantic bulbs of fluctuating size –
Now bulging vein-streaked ovoids like the Golem's,
Now wincing into tightly focused slits –
Until his REM stops dead and hits

Its hoped-for target: yes, Lyudmila's name
Illuminates a row in bold Tahoma!
The subject of her missive: "I have came"
Jolts any residue of morning coma
From Sissy, and his neurons fire with glee
And trepidation's nervous energy.

Lyudmila's note is classically Slavonic
In syntax and construction. She abhors
The verb "to be", makes charming macaronic
Neologisms, pronouns she ignores
Or genders when a sex just isn't apt,
But Sissy now decodes it, tensely rapt.

My feeling is so happy for you sending
To me one letter. Thank for you, true friend.
I'm dream to turn out fairy-happy ending
And now mine dream must maybe be pretend
No any longer, but with really life
I very like idea to being wife

With man as you, not typical, I sure.
The truly man – I tell this fact from letter –
Which can to understand me with it's pure
And simply heart. Your want for know me better
Have now for timing very many chance.
Please read to bottom with the careful glance!

I'm have the news! I will to be "on town"
(These is in English right?) to educate
Of English tongue and visiting the crown
And jewels. I'm arrive on April 8
And stayed for month and half on Vauxhall Cross
So possible will be to meet for us.

I asking so now if you want for true
To had in restaurant together meeting
For talk and see not in the simply 2-
Dimentors on computer but for eating
In same one table, breath of same one air
And possible on starting love to share?

I leave now – giving number for house mine
When I to be in city same as your
(On very soon I come!) in half past nine
O'clock the morning I have close my door
Of home if go to airport – I now crying
But not for sad, for scaring of my flying!

He's read it thrice, this joyful bright epistle,
And grasps each word and fuzzied clause *cum totem*.
His lambent nape now flares and starts to bristle.
A numinous cold palm now cups his scrotum
And tweaks a luscious nerve – this sets in train
A hypnagogic flooding of his brain.

Replying would, in Sissy's normal state,
Without this hormone rush's plosive judder,
Induce an impulse to procrastinate
But here he doesn't sense the slightest shudder
Of second thought. Our hero now composes
His answer, finds a jpeg of some roses

On Google images, which he attaches
With dexterous flourishes of expert haste;
A rare impulsiveness grips him and snatches
A verse of Pushkin. *Grâce à* cut and paste
He gives his subject field an epigram,
To guarantee it's not confused as spam.

Our hero (with each second more Ruslanic)
Proof-reads his email with an emphasis
On clarity. Approaching epiphanic
Excitement he taps in a triple kiss
Then checks himself ("perhaps that's too effete?"),
Removes two Xs with a swift delete.

BEN BOREK

The time has now arrived to click on "send".
One last check, yes, he's mentioned his choice venue –
The All Bar One that nestles on the bend
Of Margaret and Regent Streets. The menu
Provides a broad and balanced battered spread,
With something bound to turn Lyudmila's head.

So let us now repair to North West 2
Where guttural and raucous Polish hip hop
Accompanies us as we saunter through
The door and up the stairs. A lonely flip-flop
Sits mourning its lost partner as we pass
On tiptoe past the mounds of broken glass.

Perhaps there's been another artist's party.
Perhaps they live in this state all week round.
We haven't time to care about their *art de
L'escalier*, we've reached some level ground
And now we navigate the landing's floor
To Wassily's (and Iza's) bedroom door.

But Iza's out (tonight is Boxercise).
Wassily kneels beside a throbbing heater's
Regurgitating musty warmth. His eyes
Reveal relieved contentment like Demeter's
Would glow with every spring when custody
Was hers again and blossom filled each tree.

His precious foot is slowly drying out –
So picture now a muddy gaseous layer
Evaporating from around the gout-
Afflicted ankle. Breaking from his prayer-
Like stillness for an instant to adjust
His pose, he flicks an ochre clump of crust

From in between two scrawny metatarsals
And tweaks at flakes of tough, embedded gauze
That look like they're obscenely gift-wrapped parcels
Replete with livid, petrifying spores.
He then turns the whole foot upon its arch
To let the saturated instep parch.

It's nice to know you're all here by my side.
Sometimes I feel the lonesome pang my furrow
Of one-man stakeouts cuts. Come let us slide
In scale, sprout exoskeletons and burrow
Neat crannies in the welcoming nude pine
Of floorboards, prick our ears up and recline.

Wassily has a habit (most convenient
For eavesdropped narratives like ours) of speaking
Aloud and of reciting all he's seen: he went
Back home the cautious route to guard the leaking
Container from potential molestations
In lonely carriages or crowded stations.

His speech continues thus; I'll paraphrase it,
And do my best to truthfully report it.
His stutter intermittently delays it
With spluttered schwas that lengthen and contort it
Until, at times, it's one excited vowel
Remodulating like an anxious bowel:

"I have this foot, my latest body part
Of valiant Volhynians from Kresy
Who fought with all their natural Slavic heart
Under their annexed flag – theirs was, *in esse*,
Not *esse* in the least. The trichromatic
Tableau of British crosses was pragmatic

And needed any able-bodied pilot
Who had a mutual loathing of a foe
Whose will to power, brutal and inviolate,
Was signalled by a daft mustachio.
Which foe? It could be two – they would contend,
"My enemy's aggressor is my friend."

So many men fought resolute, brave, reckless,
So many souls cut ribbons through the firmament's
Thick curdled lumps of cloud and spat a necklace
Of fiery smoke that looped into impermanence
Like breaths of derring-do with plosive trails
That lassooed Messerschmitts and snapped their tails!

How many now remember 303
Squadron? The most effective in The Battle
For Britain (if you quote the BNP –
The idiots accompanied the prattle
And bilious pride upon their glossy fliers
With one of Wacław Łapkowski's Spitfires).

Apocryphal and distant winds had hissed
In childhood through Wassily's frozen ears
Of *dziadek* (granddad) lost amid the mist
Of tailspin smoke and burnt-out landing gears
That toxified the whirring theatre over
La Manche, from meek Calais to chalky Dover.

He'd heard this *dziadek* ("já-dek") hailed from Lviv
(Or Lwów – one's politics dictate the spelling)
Or "thereabouts", though here we have to give
A generous radius round the purple swelling
That marked out Lemberg (one last designation)
As less a town and more a conurbation

Upon the light-blanched map that hung, outdated
Across the walls of boyhood memory
(A bluish liver spot, its rim serrated,
Delineated Austro-Hungary).
The dot his putative forebear called home
Was lost amid the bloody spray and foam

Of military history's tsunami –
Where empires rose and fell like brawny tides –
Each generation greeted a new army
And faced a new compulsion to change sides,
(If they were fortunate), divest their farms
Or be removed by unforgiving arms.

The tale of granddad held a mystic flavour –
His parents' sleepy hamlet, or *osada*,
Where thirteen families would daily labour
On slate-flat land to stock a common larder
With beets and plump potatoes, where each hive
Of village bees was tended to in five

Slavonic tongues, where barren Aunt Svetlana
Nursed every infant at her gushing breast,
Was scene to this: one night a gaunt banana
Of crescent moon suspended in the west
Poked through a spongy wall of autumn cloud
And lit the way home for a weary crowd –

These were the settlement's thirteen strong men
Who'd harvested all day from when the cock's
Stentorian aria for the hen
Instructed them to pull on woollen socks,
Gulp down their buckwheat porridge and proceed
Towards the far horizon's rufous bleed.

And this is where the folklore gets more thrilling.
As Wassily heard tell, this weary troupe
Tramped home, backs plough-sore after hours of tilling.
Yet something fizzed and looped a lustful loop
Among them all and though their feet were tired
Their loins all flared like they were being fired

In Venus's own kiln. The snoring hives
All buzzed a honeyed coda as the men
Peeled off towards the ardour of their wives –
These women, too, had sensed a heightened yen
(More fierce than what they'd all felt every day
Of late with men too weak, once home, to play).

They waited fragrantly on heated pelts
To welcome in their menfolk with caresses,
Enthusiastically unlatch their belts
And guide their rough hands up inside their dresses.
These thirteen bedrooms melted in unanimous
Assent and as the moon watched on a clamorous

Assertion of all twenty-six lovemakers'
Loud satisfaction echoed from each shack
And far beyond, across the fertile acres
Of beet-field, off a birchwood copse and back
To ring through every ear, asleep or waking,
And leave the hamlet's nervous donkey quaking.

Refreshed and sprightly, each wife felt a glowing,
Effusive thrumming through her limbs, chest, cheeks
The following day. This grew and kept on growing
In warm contentedness for several weeks,
As did the dugs that soon ballooned and bulged
From Aunt Svetlana's blouse. Their teats divulged

Their tell-tale spreading stains of milky portent,
Though here their flooding augured something special.
So much did she produce that in her torment
She siphoned flowing quarts off in a vessel
Of painted earthenware with sharp, raw squeezes
And planned to start producing special cheeses.

This sign led every wife to hope, and soon,
Within the month, each one declared their state.
The men had all been thoroughly immune
To any wifely blandishment of late
Which led each newly-pregnant future mum
To make the same conception-dating sum.

Eight months exactly passed when thirteen males
Emerged, embalmed in amniotic oil
Like glossy pickled mushrooms with pink tails
And sodden tonsures, rust-brown like the soil
Their fathers ploughed. Her backache soothed by shock
And wild relief Svetlana ran amok,

Her blouse slit wide, a trailing lactose stream
In her excited wake. The village goats
(All underfed) lapped madly at the cream
And nuzzled round her sodden petticoats.
She kicked them off ("You brute! I'll snap your neck off!"
She cried at one) and flagged down Dr Chekhov,

Who, pedalling up a cloud of sandy fission
Around his creaking boneshaker, arrived,
As always, just too late for parturition.
No matter though, the babes had all survived
And suckled like keen cherubim – they slurped
In silence, pausing calmly to be burped.

The doctor stumbled through each natal scene
Downing a cherry schnapps each time he crossed
A happy homestead's threshold. Towelled clean
And unpicked from their teats, each babe was tossed
Into his scrawny arms and tickly prodding
Before he left amid much tipsy nodding.

A lightweight, bookish man, the young physician
Was too drunk to count to ten
And every schnapps just worsened his condition.
His digit count: "one... four... nope... once again,
One... two... five... um, theys all looks fine to me.
Toes? Yesh. Complete in wriggling harmony."

Once his rounds were done, Aunt Svetlana led him
Into the barn where he was soon undressed
And tucked up in a bed of hay. She shed him
Of cumbersome galoshes, pince-nez, vest
And with his judgement somewhat compromised
He let himself be pleasantly surprised.

Of course (you may have guessed) his numeration
Was off. The perfectly coeval eggs
Had undergone a harmless, slight mutation –
Each boy was born with seven-pronged back legs.
But love swelled like a joyous sprouting blossom
Of mutual pride throughout each parent's bosom.

The boys all grew up handsome and courageous.
And formed a merry, youthful baker's dozen.
The local fecund spirit was contagious,
It seemed, as soon they had another cousin
And, need for it now medically disproved,
Svetlana's barren prefix was removed.

The years flew past, a quiet bucolic flow
Of seasons ebbed – the summers baked the tundra,
The autumns set the rowan trees aglow
Then dimmed the massive skies as weeks of thunder
Rang out like a deep coruscating bell
And winter clouds unleashed their bitter swell.

There soon appeared a certain fey uniqueness
About the band of brothers. Not just brave,
There didn't seem to be a single weakness
Between them. They would jovially slave
Through elements unwelcoming and grim,
Their voices joined in wistful rustic hymn:

Oh, there will come a time when all the snow
Has melted in the forest and the green
Of spring awakes. Then you, my dear, will go
And wander through the pine wood's shady screen
Through needles falling down like prickly rain
And I will never see your face again!

The village farmed and harvested and flourished.
This sinewy new workforce in the fields
Increased the flow of beets and plums and nourished
The residents with record-breaking yields.
The slivovitz had never been so sweet,
Nor had the honey. Life was near-complete:

The cherry trees grew swollen with their fruit
And ringed the scene in cerasinus lustre
And pointillist green daubs of leaf and shoot
As all the youths, assisted by a cluster
Of red-faced wheezing uncles, set to hoisting
And hammering whittled beams of birchwood joisting.

Within the central square of their *osada*
The wives all looked on proud and passed up trays
Of *naleśnik* (a Polish enchilada)
And jugs of bitter lime and ice. The day's
Last sunlight now retreated, tired, and hid
Behind a blinking, dusky-clouded lid.

The deep blue lashes of the watching pines
Stirred coyly in a rustling nictitation
And there amid the gloam the ordered lines
And perfect angles of the men's creation
Reflected as a V within a tarn-
A newly varnished dancehall/schoolroom/barn.

Here elders met to soothe internal drama
And settle disputes over garden borders,
And children supervised by Aunt Svetlana
Puffed up their cheeks and blew into recorders,
(Like pasty chipmunks with long plastic snouts
They salivated drizzle from their spouts).

And soon it was a fulcrum for activity,
This *Dom Tańczący*. Neighbours from as far
As Lutsk and Sitno came for the festivity
Each month on nights when, like a branding scar
Upon a horse's jet black hide, the moon
Was perfectly halfway between her swoon

(When, arched, her thin back forms an opaque curve)
And gaping manic (one-eyed) grin. The fiddle
Stoked up the hall with vodka-sodden verve,
The balalaika's trilling pyramidal
Voice-box roused wallflowers to peel away
From shy escape and join the merry fray.

In search of bison grass and honey gimlets
Across the Lipa's drowsy, speckled waters
There came the thirteen local modest hamlets'
Unanimously favourite, sweetest daughters –
And when that autumn's run of dances ended
For winter, each had found her own intended.

And for a year or two, such youthful bliss!
If Petrarch had crept up and caught his Laura
And offered her a fresh, audacious kiss,
And she had then reciprocated for a
Deliciously, deliriously long
Embrace, this charge would not have been as strong.

This golden age was bound to end. It did.
A decade's joy was violently cut short
By geopolitics. The fragile lid
Was lifted with a simmering report
Of cannons from the crucible containing
A bellicose concoction – strained and straining,

Its elements sparred, sparked and fought for dominance;
The two moustaches rose and bid the spread
Of co-opted workforces – special prominence
Was given to the young (the nearly dead
Were helped along...). And so, in hindsight's lens
The boys were fortunate, too strong to cleanse.

The settlement changed hands, then re-changed hands,
Then once again a new force took it back.
The power *du jour* unwound the knotted strands
Of varied Slavic roots and had a hack
At all the ties that bound the population –
"Divide and rule" the clear preoccupation.

Through all ensuing strife the barn still stood,
Withstanding wayward shells and creeping flames
As if made out of Teflon-coated wood;
Once commandeered to hold those souls with names
Deemed undesirable; twice used to stash
An insurrection's homemade weapons cache…

The girls, though. Where were they? All scattered madly –
Some stolen, some just stole away. They went
By night, in brutal haste, and fanned out sadly
From home, to Tomsk, to Terezin, Tashkent
Till soon, amid the maelstrom, they dissolved –
A human jigsaw never to be solved.

The nascent love stories were left stillborn,
Forever lacked conclusive punctuation.
Their manuscripts were mercilessly torn
And burnt like acts of lost imagination.
The boys' new narrative was grim, but traceable:
They faced (and faced up to) what was unfaceable

As, separately, each lovelorn, septidigital
(Or, more correctly, septi-toed) young man
Was set to work and strain and heave and give it all
He had with axe or scythe or jerrycan.
Each one grew skinny as a rusted aerial,
Collapsed, and passed out, sweating and malarial.

They all died. Saw the tunnel. Peered deep through it.
And all perceived an evanescent light.
Oh how its deep corona flared! They knew it
Was not their time. They should return to fight.
So thirteen miracles pulled themselves back
And took a newly steeled, more earthly, tack:

No longer scared of death, but sick of slavery,
They rapidly regained their strength and shape
And, galvanised, their fierce, uncommon bravery
Grew greater yet. They planned their great escape.
With shovels, sometimes tin and sometimes flesh,
And sharpened teeth to cut the iron mesh

That cordoned them like hens on battery farms.
They used a night's confusion, when a surge
In enemy activity meant arms
From their host power's mechanised *auberge*
Were redeployed out east. Amid the fuss
They all bid *do svidanya* to the Rus.

Much tunnelling and hiding out in treetops
And undersides of carriages ensued.
(Like Ulysses escaping from the Cyclops,
Though here the sheep had wheels, their bleats were crude
And petrol-scented rumblings and their guts
Were boiling rust and caused some nasty cuts.)

The route they took is secret and oblique.
It took one lad, Maxim, the fastest runner,
Less than a fortnight's high-risk hide and seek
(You seek safe passage, hide from mine or gunner)
But Ctik travailed in ultra-cautious gear
And washed up in full drag after a year.

The bottom line is this, though – they all made it,
Somehow. And how was never once discussed.
The truth was manifest and they displayed it
Outwardly as a hardened, stoic crust –
A moistened canthus or a downturned grin
Which all belied the horrors deep within.

Arrived? Yes, on the sodden shores of Kent,
The airfields of East Anglia, the toe
That dips a rocky talon in the vent
Between the Cornish coast and Saint-Malo.
They dried off, dusted down and caught their breath
Then, to a man, they joined the RAF.

Now Polish on their papers they all served
Divisions 302 and 303:
The fighters. English colleagues were unnerved
By how there simply didn't seem to be
A single bead of nervous perspiration,
A single fearful judder or pulsation

In all these men. They made their swift ascent,
They honed in, found the whites of German eyes
And loosed their ammo's bile till it was spent.
Then down they floated through the ragged sky's
Slashed, layered sheets of crumpled azure silk
And pools of cloudy, spattered, curdled milk.

This is, as Wassily would say, "what was":
We've read the books, seen films about how "never
In the field of human conflict..." and because
We dare not spoil the fragile British weather
Which soothed the break-up of the Commonwealth
By claiming all war-glory for itself,

And hogging all the bright heroic limelight
From a junior, yet vital, partner force,
The Britishers have never found the time right
To redirect the history-river's course
And set its waters gratefully to swerving
Through rivulets unmentioned yet deserving.

Let's crawl out, Readers, I'm a little cramped
In squatting insect shape. We've heard the gist
And needn't hang around. The foot is stamped
With sea green ink – a dainty, practised twist
Of wrist and fingertips leaves it tattooed:
(My Dziadek, #13) and the brood

Of twelve is now joined by its last confrere
Beneath his bed, which crouches like a leopard
Whose menacingly fluid limbs are bare
And dappled with dark spots. I'll be your shepherd
And guide you out beyond the underwear
That festers in dank piles, and down the stair.

Wassily's monologue now nears its close.
He checks the foot – its gnarled protruding talus
(Or ankle bone), the seven rigid toes
With blackened nails (the big one like a phallus,
A crack within the nail a beady eye)
And nods as if to say: "Yes, plenty dry!"

(A deep and dusty red like Arizona,
And thankfully beginning now to reek less.)
The fat back-tendon, named after its owner,
The Classic archetypal spot of weakness
Should now be best described *Achilles' handle:*
Wassily lifts the foot into a sandal

Of cotton wool and camphorated oil.
He catches his reflection in the mirror's
Implacably sleek skin – and to the boil
Comes this emphatic thought: "Yes I am Pyrrhus!
The ancestor of greatness!" And of course
Somehow that village hall's his wooden horse.

His plan, he jabbers, hushed but piqued with pride:
To relocate the feet, repatriate them.
(It's safe to guess their owners have all died
And will not ever need to reinstate them
To walking duty.) Now with thirteen feet
The first phase of his programme is complete.

Another week has passed, another wife
Is now in order. Pink limbed, tattooed Beth
Just lacked sufficient simulated life
And so she met her animated death –
Unconsciously Tolstoyan, Neno's brain
Programmed her end beneath a creaking train.

His latest cyber-sweetheart is called Heather.
She eerily, at least in general thrust,
Recalls Lyudmila, though in more white leather
And with a more accentuated bust.
(The pixel-shaping gun has also rendered
Her nether half exotically suspendered.)

He's booked a corner table in Shakira's
And stipulated candles, violins
And Kobe beef. He's tense, but need not fear as
His Troika watch the doors. The night begins
Auspiciously, he feels, with Heather's spillage
Of furrowed bust inviting eager tillage.

There comes a point when conversation can't
Be sidestepped any longer. Until now
Though, Neno's reputation would enchant
His prey and pretty soon his foot-long prow
Would wordlessly be tugged along a stocking
To make his trademark energetic docking.

The dating game and all its etiquette
Is something new, though – how should Neno start?
"What is your favourite lubricant?" (Not yet!)
"How do you trim your hirsute second heart?"
(Oh no! That will not do! It's far too soon.)
Instead, despairing, "That's a pretty spoon."

"What do you mean?" Now Heather is confused
("If that's a chat-up line then I'm in trouble").
"I mean, well, shaped ideally to be used
To scoop up soup and sodden crouton rubble...
And, erm, that knife, it has a perfect blade...
Your fork has fingers delicately splayed

For prising steak flesh from its tender loin..."
At this point Heather puts these odd preambles
Down as strange innuendo. With her groin
Now pushed beneath the tabletop she gambles
On what she thinks the gangster wants and clinches
His pride with muscular, no-handed pinches.

Now Neno has a choice – does he erupt
In anger worthy of his fearsome name?
Does he – quite out of character – disrupt
Her willingness to play the fast-paced game?
Or does he now revert to type and ease
Her forward in her vain desire to please?

He takes the latter route. Though disappointed
That, abjectly, this dry run's sorely flopped
And any effort at a well-appointed
And civilised comportment has been dropped,
He can't quite help himself, nor quell the urge
That now arises as a throbbing surge.

So, roughly, he now meets her in the centre
And with his hands – each one a rack of ribs –
Manhandles her and, just about to enter,
He flips her round and forcefully ad libs
A move he learned last night from *Plastic Teens,*
Which played on one of Blackchapel's louche screens.

The troika, in their usual course of action,
Disperse Shakira's flustered clientele
And form a triangle of benefaction
To cheer the writhing quadrapedal swell
And clear each scattered champagne flute and plate
As the performers wildly oscillate.

I'm watching on a stream, and on a river.
(My floating home has excellent reception.)
I see how Neno, spent, now deigns to give her
A cursive little kiss. His contraception –
His method – is now keenly replicated
By Daniel, Jeb and Ham until they're sated.

Her silhouette still lingers and her glow
Is like a burnished kopek, freshly minted.
Despite the fact that she has had to go,
Its lingering remainder is imprinted
Upon my dazzled eyelids: from the nose
(A Slavic slope) down to the perfect toes.

Along its thrumming threads the DLR
Now bears her off with smooth efficiency
From Bow and her beautician. In her car
(The driverless glass-fronted helm) sit three
Plump generations of an East End clan
And their discounted spoils from Matalan.

The business world is fairly represented
By several sweating suits – all overstuffed,
All keen to cast a leer at our invented
New heroine: one midget, twice rebuffed
In efforts to engage her with his spiel
Of lines learned like a bar-room cockatiel

Now proudly hides from failure with a call:
He yanks his chirping iPhone to his ear
(A porky ampersand) and suffers all
Unfortunate co-passengers to hear
A spurious array of raucous self-
Aggrandisement straight off the dullest shelf.

Now freeze this elevated transit-scene:
A flyover by Shadwell, where a breeze
Flits cheekily around the *Crêpe de Chine*
And lacework skirt to titillate her knees
And freshly depilated calves, then tries
To edge up through the silk towards her thighs.

She has her final coat of maquillage
So, soon, I'll get the text ("all stations go!").
I'll cut the engines, moor my faithful barge
To rub against the nagging undertow
And set off on my Brompton, gaily pedalling
Towards the scene of my good natured meddling.

But wait! This costume drama's subterfuge
Is not completely done. *I* must get dressed.
I'm tired of insect life – the light bulb's huge
Electric sun leaves me purblind, my chest
Can't rise and fall, my lumber region cramps
Within a bug-sized corset's spiky clamps.

So, Readers, I've been shopping. I've invested
In garments that imply a life served at
Waxed tabletops and bars: a double-breasted
Funereal black suit, thin silk cravat
And zinc-white shirt with rose embroidery:
I'll call my look *The Sullen Maître D.*

My head fills with a rising *sonnerie*
Of vatic bells. I loop a "Butcher's Sling"
Around a helpful bollard's neck in three
Connected flowing moves – a fairway swing
Perfected on the one landlocked marina
Upon the great Red Lake in Bukovina...

Lyudmila, gentle maiden, subtle beast,
I'm proud of you! You sashay through the tunnels
Of tourists navigating from the east,
A nugget glistening along the runnels
Of subterranea along the decks
Of windswept platforms, closing on the X

That marks your entrance point upon the stage –
My pre-prepared proscenium. The spotlight
Is frantically aglow, the title page
Bleeds ink within the sweatbox of this hot night
(In a pathetic fallacy it's closer
This evening than midsummer in Formosa).

♪ The circumflex in *Maître* is a "scar".
I gleaned this from a friendly French translator.
Where once were S's, now the dented bar
Or "Szechuan Farmer's Hat" to designate a
Culled sibilant – as in *Vas y, ma bête,
Se hâter vers la tempête de ta conquête.*

The sky sweats like an inverse rippling fjiord
And dribbles spume in fierce, arrhythmic bursts;
The gutters swell around the plodding hoard
Of lolling kerbside tongues slaking their thirsts
And Phoebus lazily reclines behind
His dark, diaphanous Venetian blind.

This was the elemental tune all day
As Sissy lumbered through his office chores:
The nervous wind section pumped up to play
A run of scherzos from a brace of scores –
Commencing with a burst from Wagner's *Ring*
And settling on Peer Gynt's dark *Mountain King.*

His day cut short, his underwriters sated
With terms more generous than his convention,
He left his in-tray atypically freighted
And, with the thin excuse of his abstention
From post-work Stella in *The Nascent Men*❜
He took his leave of a suspicious Ben.

❜I have been thinking lately of my roots –
Familial, and not those subcutaneous;
My thick and lustrous mane abounds in shoots
As rich as mackerel oil which help maintain me as
A gold-crowned specimen admired in salons
Worldwide, beneath a thousand stylists' talons;

But no, my ancestry is what has roused me:
The genes that sprouted in my natal humus
And spread to form the flesh-bloc that has housed me,
My organs, blood and plasma in its rooms as
I've grown and flourished, stretched to gamely fill
This corpus with my own organic will.

Pedestrian of method, he had reasoned
That vasco-cardial enlivenment
Would leave his thinning bloodstream freshly seasoned
With oxygen-fuelled verve and nourishment
The Thameside path (North) sped in dewy flashes
Beneath his frayed and flapping Adidases.

O rush my little Juan! Stretch your gait!
Your trainers, let them cover seven leagues
With every bouncing stride. Swoop past the Tate
(These days it drops the Modern) and, as Grieg's
Mischievous little oboe clears a way
In front of you, don't dither or delay!

Now watch his undelaying dot nondithering,
Pan out, observe him on my GPS:
A Pac-Man-esque amoeba-pixel slithering
Along the asymmetric gridlocked mess
Of avenues that like a tangled nest
Grow tighter as he cuts inland, north-west.

Perhaps Wassily's occidental gaze
Has caused a clot of psychic dust to scatter
And loosed heredity's rose-fingered rays
To brighten my own pale genetic matter –
You see, my *own* forebears were rather partial
To borscht and slivovitz before the martial

Whirlwind whipped up and seared their still bucolic
Like some enraged stepfather with a temper
Erratic, knuckle-sharp and alcoholic:
My great-grandmother's eyes black seeds of hemp, her
Maternal urge relieved after a chasm
Of barren hope astride a doctor's spasm

I'll leave him in the corner of my vision
To agitate the radar at my waist
As my velocipede makes its incision
Through creaking lanes of scrap metal post-haste –
The West End, with its channels stuck like tar
Is inhospitable to coach or car.

My Brompton's slender, girlish rump and spine
Stretch out beneath my linen-coated calves;
Her soft rococo handlebars entwine
My pigskin knuckles, both her gliding halves
Throb up at me from in between their spokes
Like two ecstatic, decadent, blue jokes.

The bike rides me; the rails subsume the train;
The wheels dictate the progress of the jeep;
The slim, vibrating body rules the brain;
The castle is the servant of the keep;
The masterly, unbridled mare sustains
The hunter through the pullulating lanes.

Of frantic, bashful lust. And then her son –
Not decorously gifted with a licence
To stalk the Luftwaffe's dark swarm upon
The English Channel's cloudy rug of silence
And bursts of gunfire intermittent, clamorous,
But shunted to a station much less glamorous:

Arkhangelsk, felling trees, supping choleric
Black water as his only daily meal,
His ribcage two gaunt combs, his skin tumeric,
A shackle linking heel to withered heel.
He lugged damp timber as a gulag slave
And laid his mother in a frosty grave.

We bounce and rumble like a lazy piston
Oiled by its own components' natural lotion
Down thrilling slopes, then soaring up like Tristan
And Iseult in the heat-haze of their potion,
I settle back within the darkened dips
Of leather set between her spinning hips.

So, who will first arrive and be *in situ*
Within the boiling, oily atmosphere
Of All Bar One? Whose presence first will hit you
Between the game observant eyeball's clear
Regard? Too late! Magda... I mean, excuse me,
Lyudmila (all these sparkling names confuse me!)

Is here ahead of time and titivating
Her agitated carrot-tinted wig
(We crossed paths and endured the thrilling waiting
In mutual support). She soothes a swig
Of cold Tatanka with her pliant tongue
Which throbs delightedly and gently stung.

She looks a picture, deftly repositioning
Her petticoats (an Ingres in dusky oil).
The spinning ceiling fan's soft air-conditioning
Excites her gothic lace, her peruke's royal
(Elizabethan) golden-tangerine.
Her modest nose stud's glimmering citrine

Absorbs a swaying candle's limpid glimmer
And angles an assiduous sharp glance
Into the facing looking glass's shimmer.
Now, startled, in a lucid waking trance,
Our stumbling Sissy slowly re-emerges
Upon the waiting mirror's fulgent verges:

He grows in size with his advance approaching
Its terminus – himself (in inverse order)
With newly gel-waxed parting now encroaching
His temple from the left, not right, the border
Of sideburn fluff around his jowls more prominent
On the wrong side, right eyebrow now more dominant

And nervously alive (its back in spasm,
A drugged-up, jerking caterpillar). Shyly,
He edges as if round a yawning chasm
And slopes towards his unknown *corpus vile*,
Who now ejaculates her practised greeting:
"You shall be Sissy, so glad we can meeting."

She's perfect! How her accent's soft velarity
Commingles with its unexpected alto –
A pleasingly incongruous polarity,
Like snowflakes on the spine of the Rialto
In June, the Grand Canal awash with flakes –
A sudden rink for wayward kittiwakes.

Her movements too are so sublimely graceful
And studiedly *ad libitum*. The night
Of ardent practice, toying with a faceful
Of varied shapes to represent delight,
Demurral, deliquescence, indecision
Reaps sweet reward, such is her smooth precision!

(At times, I think I got a bit demanding
And worked her to the limit of her talent.
My patient pushing, level reprimanding
Was never meant as anything but gallant
Persuasion and assistance with her task –
I poured my heady spirit in her flask

And then, at times the job became to shake
A petite cocktail jug of raw persona
To play the man-alembic and to wake
A maiden lover fit for my Verona
From all the dense, decanted intense oils
I call my proud, essential perfumed spoils.)

But less the role of *dumny* (proud) creator,
More *chętny* (keen) observer, I attend
Their table as *wytworny* (well-shod) waiter
And catch the brooks of *czat* (chat) as they wend
Through friendly locks of discourse, splashing themes
As various as bus routes, modems, dreams...

I faint to play the killjoy typist-demagogue
But style, Dear Readers, still amounts to style.
Gross reams of quick-fire talk and snappy dialogue
Are not the thing. Instead I'll smoothly tile
Across the ragged lawn of *czat* with burnished
York stones and leave the patio well-furnished:

Needless to say that Sissy's nervous entrée
Is served and swallowed in a fit of mollitude,
For both parties have shyness served aplenty,
Both own to loving autumn sun and solitude,
The poignant minor scales in life's rich song
And feeling strangely lonely in a throng.

Her coy front now unmelts and slowly peels
At just the rate to give the sweet illusion
That someone else (or so our hero feels)
Is feeding it the warmth. The game collusion
Of widened eyes and teeth that blithely bite
Her nether-lip are saying: "That's just right".

The way she meets his sweaty glance, returns it
With interest and empathy and mirth,
Shoots something to his anxious soul and burns it
With optimism. Could this mark his birth
To full emancipated adulthood?
Sissy begins to feel perhaps it could.

And soon the barriers that dam their rivers
Of self-expression open. If we read
Our hero's inner soundtrack it would give us
An insight that we shouldn't be so dead
Of spirit not to register as pumping
With happy butterflies⁴ (his heart is thumping!).

He feels they've much in common: "We're so inward,
But now we've moved to qualified loquaciousness."
Our hero's glance but fleetingly casts sin-ward:
Such is Lyudmila's tactful, guiding graciousness
In open intercourse that Sissy's gaze
Stays transfixed in her mirror balls' twin rays

---

⁴ You must have surely once or twice had meetings
   With someone fresh and new, where an epiphany
   Of swelling joy has swamped you? How this sweet thing's
   Your perfect complement (like Grant for Tiffany)?
   How if you poured your souls into one bottle
   You'd brew love-nectar, *pace* Aristotle?

142

And rarely wanders down from their bright lights
To navigate the piles of lace and ribbon
Upon her chest or wonder what delights
May rest within their folds and might be given
As golden eggs, as prized, unbitten fruit as
Éclatant as two suns, to gallant suitors.

They slip from heartfelt chatter to perusing
The menu. Sissy comes into his own
And offers clarity to the confusing
"Beer-battered sirloin steak", "Carmarthen-grown
Organic lamb", and "Lovingly handmade
Seared plaice in Oriental tapenade".

Lyudmila's only gentle stipulation
Is "no too spicy". Sissy recommends –
To safely guard against contamination
With even the most mild of piquant blends –
The miso soup to start, with rustic roll,
And as a main a pan-fried lemon sole.

Our girl accedes, her smile now emanating
With almost tangibly light-headed pleasure:
"This is the way to play the game of dating,"
Thinks Sissy: "Nothing to it. Simply measure
Your fabric to best fit, then be as bold as
To drape your nous around the maiden's shoulders.

It really isn't very hard at all!"
He revels in his new-found self-composure.
No longer wary of a crushing fall,
He gives his *wdzięk* ("fdjenk" – charm) more bold exposure
And clicks his fingers like a gruff dictator
To summon up the wine list, and the waiter.

BEN BOREK

(He glides to centre stage on golden shoes
Armed with a tray of breadsticks, bowl of capers
And quart of Evian.) "Might Sir peruse
The specials board as well? Our range of grape has
Expanded since we made the wines you see
Before you. We've now *Durif*, *Pinot Gris*,

A plummy Napa Valley *Sangiovese*
And one or two exquisite *Tempranillos.*
I'm sorry, the sommelier is lazy
And happiest when his head's upon his pillows,
So naturally our *carte des vins* has waited
For weeks to be rewritten and updated."

The gentleman, now fully cast as alpha
(And slightly *butny* – "haughty") male consults
The grapes at random, twiddling his alfalfa
And tumbleweed coiffure (the gel's results
Are not what he had hoped for). After scanning
For long enough to give a sense of planning

He picks a Malbec halfway down the board
For reasons no more complex than its diction
("Scheurebe" has him well and truly floored)
And orders it with loud, yet fake, conviction...
Lyudmila doesn't doubt he knows his stuff,
Or doesn't seem to, which is quite enough.

The waiter shuffles decorously cellar-ward,
Moves past a gallery of paintings – princes
And potentates, an ice-glazed Russian dell or ford
(The light is poor and even if one winces
One can't make out for sure quite what is what).
There's one impressionistic khaki blot

144

Which, when observed with clarity and distance,
Suggests a beast whose scaled and squat morphology
(A tongue of flickeringly red insistence
And warty tail) belong to herpetology
And one of its sub-genuses best known as
The Shanxi (*gecko auriverrucosus*).

To dwell upon the date could seem unseemly
And voyeuristic. Readers, dearest friends,
I do sincerely hope you do not see me
As someone keen to poke his fisheye lens
Towards this scene of love's outfolding bloom
Excessively. My wish is to illume

The spectacle; please see me as a candle
Who burns with an unflinching, honest flame,
And not as some outrageous peeping vandal
With dubious and dark sadistic aim.
In my own way I'm honest, straight and sedulous,
Though understand if you find this incredulous.

But look! Don't take your bright eyes off the ball:
The Malbec has been expertly delivered.
It starts to flow and flood the tonsilled hall
Within our hero's head. (Lyudmila shivered
A wordless "no" to further alcohol.
Good girl, she must maintain her self-control.)

The first courses arrive as well: The soup
For Lydumila's mild taste-buds. Sissy chose
The braised and saffron-marinaded croup
Of muntjac fawn, served diced in four neat rows
With bloody hearts of beetroot and a *jus*
Of lingonberry, thyme and crushed bamboo.

They eat, she making sweet, contented noises,
He slathering his lips in rosy gunk.
Let us compare their peristaltic poises:
Her neck held straight, her shoulder blades and trunk
Suffused, like Rilke's torso of Apollo,
With brilliance. Just watch each dainty swallow!

He chews and swigs in tandem: grim contortion.
At times splayed outward, limbs like palsied oaks,
At others, as he forces through a portion
Of sweating meat *and* sauce *and* wine he chokes
And all his features wobble like warm tripe
Until he coughs and voids his troubled pipe.

Oh dear. I think I worry the alacrity
He's pouring down his meal with is a barrier
To conversation. Now he fills the crack that he
Has loosened, just as if a drunken farrier
De-shoed a stallion then bade it sprint
Along an alley studded sharp with flint.

He doesn't check his gorging, or his manners.
But we must make allowances – he's starved:
All day the nervous prospect, like a banner
Of slow impending doom, stretched out and carved
With fingers tremulous and cold and spiky
A hollow in his appetite and psyche.

The consequence of this: he didn't touch
A bite when he rebirthed at half-past six.
At lunchtime he forced down a modest clutch
Of roasted KP nuts and half a Twix,
But really, his gastroenteric tract
Dismissed this as a minor, opening act.

God bless Lyudmila though (and all her training)
As, even with her special English, she
Engages him, though there is no arraigning
Of his compulsive conduct. Skilfully
She now directs proceedings, making light
Of how he doesn't pause between each bite.

She asks such questions as "Where you have work?"
"Have you one sister or instead one brother?"
At one point, I perceive a reckless smirk
Though quickly she enlarges it to smother
Her self-reflective jollity beneath
An even more emphatic flash of teeth.✒

Then she continues, prodding with the gentlest,
Most unaggressive fingers one could hope for.
Her tiny hands, encircled at each bent wrist
With golden bands, let out a subtle rope for
Our hero to grab on to as he pleases.
His first response: a squawking fit of sneezes.

✒ There is a Wajda film called *Dyrygent*.
John Gielgud plays a (dubbed) returning son,
Of sorts, a famed conductor who had spent
The last three dozen years beneath the sun
And snow of *Nowy Jork* but then retraces
His flight to meet a troupe of sallow faces.

These make up a provincial troupe of players
Who toil with oboes, violins, flutes, cellos,
Privations, rations, brusque obstructive layers
Of party rules. Quite how the exile mellows,
Conducts them, tries to wearily re-visit
A romance, I forget. Don't ask "what is it?"

(A fit that Rabelaisians would approve,
Best suffered with mouth full yet not quite sealed:
Lyudmila has to tactfully remove
A clot of venison-pulp, half-congealed
Upon her geisha's neck, still half in spasm
Within its blood-red, *barszczy* cytoplasm.)

This passes by, though. Minimal disgust
Is outwardly expressed by our fair maiden
(Though inwardly she's fit to self-combust).
Her patter keeps its perkiness, stays laden
With kindly questions, strangely-stressed bright chirping,
And disregards his flatulence and burping.

The main courses arrive in swift procession:
The lemon sole and *mange tout* in a garnish
Of green pimento oil – a slight concession
To Lyudmila's soft diktat that won't tarnish
Her gastronomic pleasure – and for Sir,
A cutlet stewed in speck and flambéed myrrh.

What interests me, the reason I now raise
This film – I'd say not one of Wajda's best –
Is technical. The "Polish" voice betrays
John Gielgud's mouth, trained in the plummy west,
To such an odd degree. One can't but feel
His vocal parts are solemnly surreal.

I think of this now, well, it seems to strike me
As apposite, the frightening, *unheimlich*
Collision of a face with an unlikely
Timbre of vocal product: take a lime, lick,
And then be thrown by how its stringy flesh
Tastes like a waffle's honey-laden mesh.

Her *wdzęk* is still beyond the least reproach.
Her smile still radiates, her teeth still glimmer
(As does her sparkling diamond Shanxi brooch).
However, he is now a lonely swimmer
Who, straying into waters (here it's wine)
Beyond his depth, could use a steering line.

For want of one he takes the next-best route
And orders a quadruple Stolichnaya
With *Crème de Menthe* and pureed ugli fruit
(When mixing drinks it's best to venture higher
In concentration every time you switch,
To thus avert a dull, diluted itch).

This cocktail has its quick desired effect:
With confidence now toxically redoubled
His aim becomes to cheerily inject
The cosy parley's spluttering and troubled
Romantic engine with a potent fuel
As he now reaches for his "pecial tool":❡

❡ His date-prep took him down some foetid alleys
And dingy underpopulated by-ways
In Second Earth's uncouth suburban valleys.
He stalked the seedy joints and sped the highways
In search of sage advice for all scenarios
From grouchy courtesans and limp lotharios.

He browsed a range of unguents and charms
In covered markets, backrooms, ill-lit strip malls,
Spurned offers wild, shunned countless spangled arms,
Rejected pumps and counterfeit Rohypnols,
Until his psychic Tom-Tom, inner spaniel,
Or blunt felicity threw up a "manual":

For thirty silent seconds, eyes crushed tight,
He rootles round somewhere internally.
He slowly wins this messy, neural fight.
His booze-balmed brain's canals are twisted free:
An online booklet full of romance tips
Now filters up and hits his slurry lips.

En cour un homme poursuit une femme jusqu'à
Ce qu'elle le rattrape. Allez, cherchez la femme!
W zalotach mężczyzna uwodzi kobietę
Dopóki ona go nie usidli. Werbung heißt, ein Mann
Jagt eine Frau, bis sie ihn fängt! How he-mantises
Can vanish like so many cracked Atlantsisses!

Lyudmila takes a moment to reflect
On what she's hearing – how her paramour
Has defragmented! She must interject
To mollify this verbal shock and awe.
And so, to steer towards the shores of sanity,
She tries resetting Sissy's stretched polarity:

Its title barked its boldly manic order
To "kill a bird in one fell foolproof swoop!"
In massive type within a gothic border;
Its cover boasted an elastic troupe
Of orange body parts: refulgent chests,
Loose lips and floating disembodied breasts.

Its seller, Madame Sylvia Burlesqueoni,
Assured him, with a hybrid pout-and-wink
Of wry salacious calibre that only
A *demi-ciecle* immersed in heavy drink
And sweetly perfumed fog from fat cigars
Could grow, that "this will untie love's crossed stars,

"Sorry, not understanded. Please repeat?"
"Oh? What? Oh never mind (*What did I say!*)"
Lyudmila does her best bemused-but-sweet
And delicately pulls a foot away
Before it's crushed. "Just something that I read.
The *London Lite*. Must have stuck in my head."

His next recourse, now memory starts to straighten out
From deep beneath the layers of cocktail sauce,
Is *posture* (booklet, p.9). Limbs are shaken out
Of lactic build-up "*By the second course
One's thighs can stiffen,*" he mumbles, and aligns
His feet with hers. "*The first non-verbal signs*

*Are all expressed with symmetry, or lack of it.
Imagine that your date's your mirror image.
Sounds odd? But persevere. You'll get the knack of it
And balance out the energy.*" A scrimmage
Of squeaking rubber soles and scraping castors
Now buckles up against the plush pilasters.

————————

Unbutton Eros's tight-cinched straightjacket,
Set free a flood of ardour through your channels.
If you now sense a crushing joyless lack, it
Will disappear as cupid's dart impanels
A jury full of skin as sweet as fudge
For you to delectate as noble judge!"

The latter chapters were diagrammatic
(Sissy had turned directly to the gloss
That promised pictures). Here, each gauche schematic
(The Eight-limbed Bull, The Cone, The Southern Cross)
Held arcane inspiration. He exploded. It
Was too good to resist. So he downloaded it.

He twangs a blind big toe against the blunt,
Unfeeling table's spine, kicks out in pain
First sideways (a dumb "thwack") then out in front
In witless reflex, whacks the leg again,
Then somewhat straightens up and spits a grin
As his poor date withdraws a laddered shin.

His palms he lays face down upon the slab
Of pine. Beneath the candlelight they spray
Grim shadows, like a bloated, black-clad crab
In union with a five-spiked manta ray.
The table (here's what wooden parts are for)
Takes up the inert role of ocean floor.

And, no... he isn't? Yes, he reaches forward
With both of his damp pincers, pins Lyudmila's!
Her instinct – to recoil and steel her craw would
Be fatal. She resists, observes the drill as
Was practised and prepared-for. This is tense.
I promise her a generous recompense.

She does, thank god, compose herself. Recalling
Her mission – gently nudged. My gracious waiter
Encouraged her while tactfully installing
An Evian re-fill on the equator
That nervously divides the two stained states
Of geyser wineglasses and Lakeland plates.

He paid the Madame 50 *SE Lira*
And added, with a mafioso's candour,
A hearty tip-in-kind ("should Madame fear a
Competing gang demanding a backhander
To keep her stall intact...") then sweating, squinting,
Unzipped his pdf and set to printing.

So now he spills a messy cataract
Of sweet talk – oh how all that alcohol
Has numbed his pudic muscles, and his tact!
But first, before he loosens crude-control,
He sputters more *aperçus* from his booklet:
"Don't be a modest chef or cautious cook, let

Your natural spices simmer out in talk,
Don't hesitate in sprinkling excess garnish
When speaking of your talents, walk the walk
Of course, but it is not a sin to varnish
Your runway with some choice exaggeration
About your high position's lofty station...

A woman loves to hear these things – just trust
Us, we've helped up to ⟋ *millions in the battle.*
Emblazon your appeal, buff up your crust
Of manliness, perfect your sabre's rattle
With jewels of your achievement and prowess
Remember: more is more, and less is less."

To rival a suburban Hercules
A ream of virtuosic labours pours
Straight off his tongue in slurring journalese:
He earns a mint, his word can open doors
Locked fast to lesser mortals, Usain Bolt
Requested sprinting tips ("a charming colt"),

⟋ Then, later, after several more eruptions
  He'd switched off *Second Earth* to rest his battery's
  Old lithium cell (these technical abruptions
  Assuage mum's night-sweats too) and turned to *Flattery*,
  First chapter in the book's handwritten half,
  Wherein he read this gnomic epigraph.

He turned down Spurs, Milan and PSG
(Just didn't see the challenge) has degrees
From Cambridge, Oxford, Yale, the LSE,
Speaks passable Norwegian and Maltese,
He drives a Bentley Mulsanne – customised
To leave the steering shaft less compromised...

The list grows longer, only breaking stride
In mad expansion to permit a swig
Of several more concoctions – now he's tried
My Max Wall-Banger, Adam's Flaming Fig,
Bulgakov Margarita and Dark Gimlet
(With minerals from a shady Volga inlet).

Lyudmila smiles while inside Magda frowns
(Unnoticed, he's too smashed) as here a slurry
Of noxious compliments (more Neno Brown's
Than Sissy's own authentic flinch and worry)
Begin to permeate the one-track discourse:
His tongue is positively sopping, viscous,

As intimations to the poses struck
Between them flow much less as intimation
Than in a graphic train, truck after truck,
All juggernauts of hackneyed film-citation.
(And *cinema* is really not the word,
The movies Sissy watched were more absurd

Last night he'd skimmed this. The first paragraph
Read simply, in a friendly chatty style.
It spoke of complimenting, making laugh,
Of complementing too, and making smile,
Of tactile tactics, touches best employed
To leave your lady coyly overjoyed –

Than *The Discreet Charm of the Bourgeoisie*
Played backwards, upside down, at triple speed
In badly dubbed Polari. Should you see
In some lubricious den in Pontypridd
Or Sharm el-Sheikh scenes even close to those
He took his twisted cue from you'd impose

An instant moratorium, entreaty
Your recollection "wipe!", beg Mnemosyne
To fail you, bleach away the mind-graffiti
And any residue from that vile screen.)
Our girl sits passive through the whole benighted
Soliloquy. And I look on, delighted.

His speech is more a Hamlet than a Banquo –
Our boy is far from dead, though barely sane.
However, most unprincely Sissy's rank flow
Is odd: he speaks but then hears back again
(As if bounced off the watching green-eyed gecko)
His nonsense – he's Narcissus *and* his Echo.

Another blue-mouthed minute grimly passes.
A dinner scene with Neno is recalled
(An evening in Shakira's): Empty glasses
Appear to flood with blushing steam, appalled.
And Sissy, too, grows morbidly aware
Of how he's spouting odorous hot air.

The kind of tips pale bedroom-bound young men
Receive from ever-helpful lifestyle sites
Like *Elle* (viewed on a mum-proof VPN),
Where "confidence" and shoes have equal rights
Within the pantheon of wisdom blent
Inside a giddy cloud of gaudy scent.

But he can't stop it. Like a reckless Mallard
With brakes malfunctioning he carries on
Despite himself, and offers scenes that Ballard
Might just have self-censorially forgone.
He hears himself (but not him, an intruder
With his voice-box) go further, deeper, cruder.

Yet simultaneously he's enjoying it.
Some part of him – his diabolic twin –
Delights in all this filth and keeps deploying it.
He's fighting with himself, so cannot win,
But spins in contradictory espousal
Of two extremes – contrition and arousal.

Lyudmila laps up every word. This too
Is disconcerting for his saner half,
Which knows that any normal girl would slew
And wriggle in uneasiness, not laugh
And wink an eyelid's glitter-dusted awning
In gay response to his outrageous fawning.

The devil on his shoulder disregards this
And tells the angel on the other, "Shush,
She loves it. Keep it up! Your fear retards this
Inexorable march, slows down the push
Towards my goal – the manful annexation
And plunder of this young adjacent nation."

The angel cowers, chastened, and the devil
Conducts proceedings with his three-pronged baton.
He cranks things up another vulgar level:
Lewd boast, large swig of drink, long leer: this pattern
Repeats, intensifying every verse –
The swigs and leers stretch out, the words get worse.

And all the while the angel squirms in horror,
Disgusted at his own *zły brat* ('bad brother')
Whose language is a dark, verbose Gomorrah.
He wonders how they issued from one mother
And tries, in vain, to lock the vocal catch
From out of which these frightful pictures hatch.

No use. The horse has bolted. Stable doors,
Enamel drawbridges, portcullis canines
All close too late. The river madly pours
And pauses only when our hero mainlines
A boozy tributary to join the gore
That gurgles like a drunken Severn bore.

And now Lyudmila sees the scene unravel
Exactly as her loving coach had told her.
She loosens her tense glutes, dispels the gravel
Of nervousness she's sat on to unfold her
Translucent legs and fills her diaphragm
With fresh content. Her grin spreads like bright jam.

A gleeful Naiad, mischief-merry elf,
Assumes her glowing features: her companion
Is tangled in a mess of briny self.
His concentration skirts above a canyon
Of stuttering deflation (Colorado
Of shame). Just airborne, flapping flushed bravado,

He hovers, stomach-spun, upon that liminal,
Uneasy strip of airspace – it can't last,
As, Readers, even in the realm subliminal
The force of gravity obtains, and fast.
The force of alcohol is also growing
And Sissy, bladder-wracked, risks overflowing.

A timely toilet break: I wash my hands,
Observing how he fumbles in the grease
And limescale of the mirror, how his glans
Is glazed pre-emptively and throbs cerise.
Przepraszam (sorry) if this is *de trop*,
Or TMI (more than you'd wished to know).

He flaps his nozzle dry and reinserts it.
Now startled at his own embattled face
He flees towards the hand-driers and deserts it
To fend alone then slowly self-erase
And fade beside my own evaporation:
A four-eyed, double-headed sublimation.

But wait, before he drags each withered limb
Back up to reassume its recommended
Position, let us take a look at him:
His face is soaked. (The bathroom tap forefended,
With iced handfuls across his facial stover,
What Nabokov would call a "boiling over".)

This also clarified his failing vision –
Which now explains his flight from his reflection –
The sudden auto-baptism's provision
Of focus leaves him pondering his direction;
Somewhere, within his brainpan's boozy stewing,
He knows how truly awfully he's doing.

The corridor outside the wet-tiled gents
Becomes a scene of strained *recueillement.*
The beer-and-crisps and toilet-soap ferments,
A shroud of distant chat drifts nonchalant
Around his ears, an obscure cloud develops
And floods inside, then blossoms and envelops.

He leans an awkward elbow on the wall
And spills a deep-lunged, bronchus-busting sigh.
I know this is a trope that you will all
Have tired with by this juncture, but my eye
Can only apprehend and then report
What plays out in the boundaries of its court.

My other eye, omniscient and lizard-like,
Espies my dearest Magda back upstairs.
With nimble, rapid movements, deft and wizard-like
We click our heels then join her unawares –
Just like a Murakami youth, she's scouring
Her fingernails with toothpicks, thoughtful, glowering.

But as she hears his footsteps on the staircase
She straightens up her birdlike back, re-points
Her smile, nimbly rejuvenates her hair, face
And welcoming, soft posture, reappoints
Lyudmila to her central, starring role
And waits with calm, professional control.

She knows there won't be long till Phase the First
Has reached its slick completion. One last push
Of shocking gestures, expertly rehearsed,
Should help inflate a virtual Hindu Kush
Of rocky and impassable finality
Up through the dark terrain of the locality.

And now the time has come. Our sopping hero
Returns and sits back down, after a fashion.
His shirt, once white, is now a blotchy Miro
Of reds and oranges – a wholesome ration
Of well-earned dinner has returned to blemish
His breast, loosed in a fit of coughing Flemish.

She wastes no time: "Excusing me for going.
I down to baths-room for to change my dressing.
You must to order desert. I unknowing
Which taste has best. And what means Eton Messing?
I cannot also know how is Alaska
Been baked!" How well she sets back to her task! Her

Lithe tongue remodulates to curve her trill
In upward, rolling waves. She draws a spiral
With one ideally tiny heel until
She's upright and departed past the viral
Effluvium on Sissy's dampened chest.
She's very *mądra* (wise): some space is best.

He mumbles something after her – its clarity
Is hardly crystalline. My tender ear
Though hears him meekly note the popularity
Of triple-toffee sponge. (The Brigadier
Now swims into the windscreen on his thoughts'
Lost highway – "Dad" devoured those sticky tortes...

As quickly as he came he melts away though,
And fizzles in a puddle by the gutter
As now, before our hero's eyes, a dayglow
Parade of morphing Rorschach blobs all splutter –
You know, the slightly nauseous, sense-surprise
You're met with when you tightly close your eyes...)

This scene is drawing on though, and I'm tiring.
I can't indulge in Sissy's febrile thinking
Much longer, can't sift through his mangled wiring
To find much sense. There's one clear strain: "more drinking!
So forthwith I deliver my expedient
Chat Noir with added mystery ingredient.

He guzzles down my delicate admixture
And sinks his fast-revolving head between
His clammy hands as every joist and fixture
Spins numbingly. His pulsing thoughts careen
And bump upon themselves in Brownian motion
As sweat embalms his cheeks in pungent lotion.

Now she returns! Our freshened-up Lyudmila
Trots back doused in *Un Jardin sur le Nil.*
Oh look, she's changed her clothes. Now dressed to kill a
Small tribe of teenage boys, her lips congeal
And loosen with each small electric flinch,
Her eyes hold Sissy's in a steady clinch.

Her wardrobe switch: a fishnet body-stocking
With multi-coloured appliqué in rills
Around her aureoles. Three interlocking
Gold hoops keep it one-piece about the gills.
Is there another tactful, sequined cluster
Below? Our boy can't look – he's too afluster.

She takes her seat. She asks him, "Are you choose?"
(He has. Cheesecake, two spoons – the sponge is off.)
"And kaffe creamy?" (yes) "And how mine shoes?
You liking them?" "Um" (gulp) "Um, yes... um" (cough):
She swings her legs *à la* pre-war Berlin,
As though Miss Bowles possessed her from within.

"New fitout best for dancing, nyet?" "Um..." (quiver)
"You mean you want... um, me? Um... you? Um... *danc*ing?"
"We go to diskotek!" She spoons a sliver
Of trembling cheesecake mouthwards, gamely lancing
With hungry fangs a hapless maraschino.
Poor Sissy's gone as white as an albino.

Oh, this is all too much for him. (And me:
I must apologise, but while she changed
I helped myself to just a little free
Chianti as I artfully arranged
The bleeding berries round the cheesecake's crust
And prepped its bubbling face in cocoa dust.)

I'll fade away stage left, a noble gas,
Emerge, solidified, beneath the beaming
Spotlight of moon on clouds like sheening bass.
The mandatory yellow *dym* (smoke) steaming
In dumb volutes from in between the drains
And scudding wanly over Soho lanes.

So what from hereon in ensues I'll vouch for
A little later, once I have the tapes.
I'll find an easy chair, commodious couch or
Chaise longue from which to view the evening's scrapes.
But, yes, for now it's best if I shut down
My correspondent's pen to rest my crown.

Goodnight sweet princes, goodnight sweet princesses!
Goodnight my dear sultanas, goodnight barons!
Goodnight tsarinas, tsars, counts, baronesses!
Goodnight Olivias, Waynes, Cuthberts, Sharons!
Good night Lyudmila, good luck on the dance floor,
And thank you – you did more than I could ask for.

My cabin is Ukrainian deluxe:
A matching shagpile wallpaper and carpet,
Saucepan-sized lavabo that breathes and sucks
A tenebrous black pool – a soapy tar-pit –
And felted quilting on a blunt couchette❜
Beneath a "shelf" (a black, wall-mounted net).

I have a dongle (wifi networks here
Are intermittent and, besides, too prone
To infiltration's nosy eye and ear)
Which helps me access, via Android phone,
A useful archive of what's lately been:
A cable's help connects my laptop screen.

❜ Oh locomotive train! I say "pociąg",
An onomatopoeic noun so true
It has no betters! (rhymes with "bong along!"
And beats belch, splash, neigh, chatter and achoo)
Repeat it now: por-chóng por-chóng! We're traveling:
A picaresque green woodland lane unravelling!

BEN BOREK

"But where exactly are we?" you're now asking.
Well, Readers, let me plot the languorous course for
Your records. Here a rusty signpost basking
In milky frost says "eight versts outside Warsaw".
But don't let that unnerve you... it's geography
That doesn't yet concern our shared orthography.

So as we trundle through the vales and dells
Of winter-numb Mazovia we'll review
Some previous scenes from Cricklewood. That smells
Don't email yet – thank god! A sea of glue
And fixative is rising through the eaves,
Some stuck in nostrils, some on Magda's sleeves.

A storyboard adorns a wall-length screen
Within her studio's usual disarray
Of piled-up books (*Venus im Pelz, Justine...*)
And DVDs (*Quills*, *Salo, Groundhog Day...*).
A dozen naked bulbs all flare to scatter
Dark shadows on discarded cultural matter.

Those Copydex-encrusted sleeves lie flat
And lifeless, though. The artist can be seen
Upon a futon, purring – less a cat
And more a dormant, charging thought-machine
With every flinching, dreaming nerve suggestive
Of deep subconscious work, controlled but restive.

What is her dreaming? We can but surmise.
I might propose that she has somehow entered
Cezanne's "Barnes" *Bathers* (how her busy eyes
Protrude their film of lid, and don't lie centred
And still suggests as much). I see her features
Jump freely between eight matt-blotchy creatures.

Then snap! She's up with us, and fit to prance like
A nyala with sinewed calves and tendons.
With instant wide-awakeness and a dancelike
Proficiency, her hair's bunched rhododendrons
Are scooped and fed through bright elastic bands
By hyperactive fingers, dexterous hands.

She grabs a few loose-lying Polaroids
And snorts a little satiated sneeze
Then pins them to the wall, to whitewashed voids
That welcome them like ships to stormswept quays,
Then steps back to contentedly observe
Her storyboard. Its content I'll reserve.

I have to. *Es muss sein*. The lower deck
Of our good ship is grumbling into being
And threatens to extend its meddling neck
Around the corner of the scene we're seeing-
By this I mean that Wassily is stirring
(My fish-eyed, pre-mic'd sensors are unerring).

———————

And, as with any dream slideshow's fluidity,
Magda is now all five pink *Demoiselles
D'Avignon* – with the modern local quiddity
Of gleaming nostril piercings. Tinkerbell
Soon flutters round those apertures and, true to
Her fairy type, she flaps a Prada tutu...

...which now a mermaid tail, now magic rug,
Wraps up a starred kaleidoscopic vista
With fluid strokes, a sweeping silken hug
Round Magda, Magda, Magda's perfect sister
And lookalike twin aunties Magdalena
And Maggie in a glittering container...

So, cut to camera 2 – an overhanging
Wide-lensed affair concealed in an Ikea
Häggås lamp: half-dressed, Wassily is banging
Fat nails into something. What could it be – a
Toy sailing boat with balsa wood propeller?
A set of sanded shelves for Izabela?

Oh no. Wassily's frantic DIY
Is not concerned with normal domesticity.
The camera's zooming, fast-dilated eye
Depicts a shape of wilful eccentricity –
A massive purple suitcase (Tinky Winky)
The size of a young whale – a sperm, or minke.

But what for all the toil with nails and hammer?
Valises don't come flat-packed/self-erectable!
Of course not. But if you intend to cram a
False bottom in to render undetectable
The thirteen legless feet that you've long stored
Beneath your bed (your "multipedal horde")

...which now is Duchamp's rainbow-cracked *Large Glass*
But pint-sized and cylindrical, replete
With *malinowy* (raspberry) juice and kvass
Which pours itself in arcs both cold and sweet
Towards a pair of quilted Dali lips;
Magda now purses, pulls susurrant sips.

The air exhaled is flung across the floor
In Cubist angulars (a violin,
A green, prismatic face). They seed and spore
A roguish gallery of pain, within:
A stained vitrine, a pope's engorged black mouth
Screams out beneath a paint-bleed falling south;

Some sweat and blood will naturally be shed
And flow along your straining dorsal curves:
Some magic metal – cadmium and lead,
Some *trompe l'oeil* carpentry that slyly swerves
The casual viewers' eyes to make believe
There's nothing up the case-holder's loose sleeve.

He has his feet all bagged up, swaddled soft
In extra gentle gauzy layers of wrapping
And in they go, tucked tight within their croft
Of padding, cotton wool and careful strapping.
So now the rest of Tinky Winky fills
With Wassily's own chattels, shirts and frills.

This act of packing done, the camera follows
As Wassily, his suitcase safely locked,
Now bumbles up the stairs with claret hollows
Around his manic eyes, his neckline pocked
With craters that erupt in scarlet blooms
Whenever nervous energy assumes

An elongated humanoid extends
Improbable long limbs of lava-bubble,
Its face a dented shadow, ribcage bends
In on itself, then all its members double
And grow to spider out and plant sharp feet
In Cricklewood, on Magda's sleeping street.

Defying waking limitations (headroom
And gravity specifically) this shape
Now scuttles through the window of her bedroom
And, spilling flakes of gold-leaf ticker tape,
Re-enters Magda's consciousness, uniting
Two dreaming levels under moody lighting.

A dominant controlling role within him:
He also has a fog of unwashed odour
That travels up the flight (it wouldn't win him
An armpit of the month prize, its tarte coda
The camera has to bravely navigate
(Nose held) till it hits Magda's bedroom gate).

Now Readers you must surely have endured
A conversation full of strained concealment.
What follows, just thus: Magda has obscured
Her wall-length plan beneath a blurred enlargement
Of castles, elephants and gnomic maps
So now she's primed for Wassily's keen raps.

She welcomes him: "Hej! Bored? Where's Izabela?"
"She's Boxercising, I'm a little restless.
Have you been busy?" "Nope. Not much to tell. A
Brief spurt of energy helped make this necklace
Of ancient pubs that ring the Northern Line...
Not much else though... how have you been?" "Oh, fine!

I've written reams of my new tract, attacking
The mainstream Western gangs of thinking-sentries.
You know, the usual." "Sure!" now Magda, backing,
Calm, bedroomwards, affords the politest entries
"Come in, sit down, tell me of all your planning!"
(Now camera 3 keeps pace with rapid panning.)

"I think that I might travel overseas,"
Says Wassily. "Oh? Where?" "Nothing specific.
Perhaps Galicia, the *fleur de lis*'
Last lingering death mould..." "That sounds terrific!"
Says Magda, "whenabouts might you depart?"
"Quite soon, I guess. But what of your new art?"

"The Russian maidens project? It's developing.
Can't give *szczególy* (details) but it's safe
To say that it's been passively enveloping
My day-to-day existence." Our dark waif
Now sits down on her futon, with her palm
Pats mattress: *sit down here, I'll do no harm*.

"Dziękuję" (thank you). "Nyema za shto" (nothing!)
"I think that I might travel soon, too." "Yeah?
To where?" "Oh. I don't know" (her well-trained bluffing
 Now takes flight. Magda lists the Scottish air,
The wide Hellenic sun, the Schwartzwald moss,
Le Mont-Saint-Michel, some long-abandoned schloss).

The doubly formed duplicity continues
Between them. He now reaffirms the wrong
Galicia by talking up the venues
In Spain that pique his wanderlusting song:
He mentions A Coruna, Finisterre...
She listens, grins, and twirls her raven hair.

They chat on, sharing Cutter's Choice crumbs, Magda
Deferring all more concrete inquisition
Towards her art, her trip, which new muse has her
Enlivened, questions of her true position
Politically, artistically, and why
She hasn't cleaned the bath since last July.

And now a bottle (Absolut) emerges
From deep beneath her sheets. Their loosened tongues
Unnerve me. Will my dearest thaumaturge's
Dark magic plant itself upon the rungs
Of Wassily's keen ladder of suspicion?
No fear! She keeps her sober disposition.

After an hour they part, her storyboard
Stays hidden. Wassily hears Izabela
Returning. His domestic duty-chord
Plays through him. He prepares a mortadella
And grilled shitake stroganoff with pitta
And *ostry* (spicy) garlic dip to greet her.

Despite his vodka intake, dinner passes
The test. His wife is flushing pink and beaming
(Endorphins from her Boxercising classes
Are sparking through her thrumming blood and streaming
Towards her levelled brain and busy heart).
"That augers well", thinks Wassily. "Good start."

He now, along with toasted bread, must break
The news that he'll be heading east tomorrow.
Her lie-detector, honed to spot a shake
Of timbre by a megahertz, won't swallow
Soft, white lies, nor those eggshell, taupe or black.
So he treads this initial, gentle track:

"My Sweetheart! Oh my catkin of the valley!"
"What do you want?" (Track one is up in flames.)
"I have to go away. It's Auntie Sally."
"Your aunties all have Belarussian names."
"You're right. Oh silly me. I stand corrected."
(Track two is likewise rapidly rejected.)

He knows, with heavy heart, there is but one
Sure, foolproof trick to bending Iza's will.
At times like this he has to set the sun
On any chance of bedroom joy until
His wife relents. To license his caprices
He threatens drought, withholds, makes sure, releases.

"I think that little Wassily is sickening.
He's limp and pale and wouldn't stand up well
To any sweet attempt at blood-flow quickening.
He shouldn't put the devil back in hell..."
And Izabela's heard enough. "Okay!
You leave. That's fine. When do you go?" "Today."

"Today? But it's the middle of the night!"
"Precisely. So the day has just begun.
Relax." Relieved, a playful twinkling light
Returns to Iza's eyes. "The rising sun
Is hours away, and I'm *so* energised.
Sure Waszylito cannot be surprised?"

Now camera 4 retreats upstairs behind them
And with instructions from a lewd producer
The sepia-tinted shot now cuts to find them
In soft porn mode: seductress and seducer
United in their nightly rediscovery
And Waszylito's sudden full recovery.

The music pipes in: rosy chunks of Rhodes,
A slappy bassline, stabs of plastic flute,
Until the mawkish saxophone unloads
Its tinny whirlwind. Now's the time to shoot
The happy pair from an unlikely angle
As eight slim limbs, two greedy tongues entangle.

Convention would dictate a cut like this
(One made-for-TV, late night, Channel 5):
A climax (synchronised) a tender kiss
Then morning – marbled kitchen, Five Alive
And steaming coffee, her in loose white shirt
(His Ralph Lauren), his pecs well-waxed and pert

Above his towelling kaftan. Both complexions
Immaculate; no gooey morning eyes;
Their teeth white phosphorus. Their bronzed reflections
Both shimmer in the camera. Bacon fries
With sonorous hot pops. A healthy flood
Of sunlight dries their hair and warms their blood.

This is all *lovely...* but it's Santa Barbara,
Not Cricklewood. There is no airbrushed spread
Of nutriments, the London sky won't harbour a
Beneficent fat sun. They're still in bed
And, having woken thrice to penetrate
The pleasure zone, both look a well-drained state.

Wassily is the first to break his slumber
(As usual) and he slinks downstairs for tea –
He likes it black and strong – a steaming umber
With just a hint of stirred-in chicory.
He checks his mental list and ticks off: cash
(Pounds, złoty, hrivna), food (rusks), false moustache.

We'll split the screen now, leave him sipping, scratching,
While upstairs Magda whirls within a bluster
Of petticoats, wigs, socks (some odd, some matching).
Two piles emerge: one wild, discarded cluster,
The other is a neatly folded mound
In which Lyudmila's favourite slips abound.

Her packing protocol is clear – take nothing
That looks as if it came from west of Krakow.
No telltale Marks and Spencer's bras, no cuttings
From *Zeitgest*, no maps scribbled on the back of
Zone 1-7 travelcards, not any
Rogue currencies – no euros, not a penny.

No National Insurance number, no
Secreted cans of Speckled Hen or Stella,
No photographs of Brighton in the snow,
No pen-and-inks of naked Izabela
And Wassily, no data-sticks with stored
Flash files pertaining to her storyboard.

Her storyboard! Yes, I had quite forgotten
With all that movie talk and careful camerawork.
So let us peel its veil of flapping cotton
And see how Magda deigns to mount and cram her work –
Her impish nerves in patterns on a screen –
In shapes that all obey the golden mean:

A timeline runs around its edge in black
The months and days are marked in scarlet crayon:
Like time were just a cyclical dirt track
For gashes, cuts and spurting wounds to play on.
The first mark (cross-hatched X) of real conviction
Dates back to page one of our current fiction.

We see a handsome gentleman *en velo.*
He weaves in front the spectrum of boutiques
On Rye Lane Peckham, bunny-hops a yellow
Appeal for Witnesses (ignored for weeks)
And spins his Brompton's pedals, rings its bell
Then cuts across the Common's Blakeian dell.

The second run of photos, second scratch
On time's dark vein: a pair at breakfast, mumbling
And sipping tea – their pallid features match –
His pinker though, hers crinklier. While fumbling
For errant toast the mother bends, revealing
The ventric swell her nightgown's been concealing.

BEN BOREK

The third batch (dated later that same day):
The same young man from breakfast, suited, seated
Before his lunch companion's matching grey
Bouffant and three-piece suit. Their mugs depleted
Of tepid tea, one broods, one shovels down
A Cinnamon Bonanza's black-iced crown.

The circle spins, events are marked by screen-shots
From dating sites (all with an eastern focus)
Artistic prints from Russian magazines – pots
Of Russic Ginger hair dye, Black Sea Crocus
Mascara, Perestroika matt concealer
And Sylvain armpit-spray called Philomela.

Magda has also flexed her sketching hand –
Small portraits, mostly charcoal stabs and smears,
Of Neno Brown and Doberman, his band
Of three malignant, red-eyed musketeers.
His string of stylised womenfolk appear, as
Does that momentous evening in Shakira's.

There are a clutch of emails ("froms" and "tos")
Signed S and L, a log of web activity,
A password "'password"!) wrapped in see-through glue's
Tough layer of bubbling, amber-thick captivity.
Abounding too are shots from *Slavic Beauties*
And rival sites *Bolsh-Joy* and *Russian Cuties*.

The narrative upon the board is peppered
With *objets trouvés*: ticket-stubs to Bow,
Off-cuts of fabric (ersatz snake, faux leopard)
Three glued-on cut-glass vials of best Bordeaux
(These Sasha from Dubrovnik left undrunk)
And buds of piquant, orange-blossomed skunk.

And now, the meaty part, pinned on this morning:
The nightclub scene I sadly had to skip.
Lyudmila, liquid-legged, bending, fawning,
Her dance-moves spun with Arabica hips,
Her partner squirming, glazed in drunken sweat,
His shirt ripped off, his gooning rictus set.

Eventually it seems they're asked to leave –
Their flaming double Absinthe-fizz set fire to
An inattentive barmaid's ruffled sleeve.
The snapshots here reveal that they retire to
A Vauxhall dungeon – when examined closely
It seems less David Mellor, more Max Mosely.

Moreover, it's familiar. The banisters
Have greasy fingerprints I recognise
And, framed above the Gecko-decal balusters,
A pair of keen, reptilian-red eyes...
Which means that... if I just click on this icon...
Oh good, it's playing fine. I'd left the mic on.

This option here: "play video", that's super,
Enlarge the screen... good... plug my headphones in.
(Sennheiser CX 50s with a loop for
The fibreoptic flex and gold jack-pin.)
The graphics now take flight within a layer
Of jumping fuzz on Windows Media Player.

Well, Readers, though I can't condone the stealing
I watch this video in my couchette
And just don't have the heart to start revealing
The dripping cavalcade of grease and sweat
Nor could I find the words to fully capture
The scale of Sissy's dark, *unheimlich* rapture...

So I'll employ the *Pregnant Widow*▸ mode
And tell you this much – something big took place.
A *thing* of *big* proportions. Something strode
Across the maculate, pocked inner face
Of Sissy's psychic globe and rearranged
The gaunt topography and left it changed.

––––––––––––

▸ So, yesterday I read *The Pregnant Widow* –
Apparently "a true return to form".
Soaked, naturally, in fragile male libido,
It deals with weathering the social storm
Of sexual revolution from the view
Of little "Keith", who's really you-know-who.

In keeping with the darkly laughing oeuvre
(Including poor, ill-treated *Yellow Dog*)
That Amis Jnr has presided over,
The id his *Gog,* the ego his *Magog,*
The superego wry and fatalistic
His characters self-consciously hubristic.

There is a strange, potentially perverting,
At very least perverse, scene two-thirds through.
The callow Keith starts broodingly exerting
His sexual "magnetism" (what to do
If you are 5'6", pale, unathletic
Except to *talk* beyond the mere cosmetic?).

He first directs his glum, unnoticed charms
At blonde, oft-topless, bronzed Sheherazade
(I should now clarify – the sunkissed arms
And publicly-borne breasts and legs bombard
Poor Keith, unleashing wanton psychic drool,
Because they're all stretched out beside the pool:

An airy Tuscan Villa/small Castello,
The early 70s – a *Country House*
Style comedy of manners). Burnt morello,
Chain-smoking, cramming Eng-lit, Keith the grouse
Sits hot behind his shades, inflamed, perspiring
With Lilly (girlfriend who he's stopped desiring).

I'm rambling to my point – that backdrop's plenty:
He doesn't get Sheherazade (unlikely
At best, Keith toxified the slimmest scent he
Might have attracted her with). One dark night he
Does chance upon the novel flesh he craves –
An incident that scars in psychic waves.

It's Gloria (née Beautyman) the provider
Of what it is I want to represent.
Perhaps Keith's memory, like the Cern Collider,
Span round the neural pain of the event
And let it all explode in willed obscurity
And thus expunge its scandalous impurity.

The only concrete thing we know is this:
Something unspeakable occurs aesthetically
(Unless there's something glaring that I miss)
That leaves poor shell-shocked Keith to ache pathetically
And mope around the manor in a daze,
Face shielded from the sun's malicious rays.

THREE

Dear hello Sissy, hoping you have fine?
I writing on this moment for enquire:
Your having still same fantasy with mine?
We will make meeting with again same fire
And passionful romancing? I have right!
(With hope we love us not just by one night?)

The pity very huge I must to left
From Vauxhall in today on half to noon.
When came to airport feeling was bereft
But full of hoping that I sea you soon
On village where is simples home for me,
Mine ducks, mine sheeps and all mine family!

Not certain yet for me which home is best
When we have marriage. Can be Vauxhall Road,
Or can be Beresteczko; can be Brest
Or can be Cricklewood. True love was showed
For us the last night (and found too true pleasure!)
No rush-hour, we decide details "by leisure".

Our boy reciprocated, tossing off
A missive, brief yet earnestly composed.
Its essence: "Yes! I am your Molotov
Packed full of febrile fuel! Just keep me hosed
With balmy touch and soothing ministration.
I cannot breathe for fear of conflagration!"

And then he squirmed outside, performed a spin
Upon a chubby heel (his sorry head
Complained and doubled up that spin within).
He stilled himself and "Listen, mum," he said,
"I need to ask a lady if she'll marry me.
She's far away. I think you'll have to carry me,

At least sometimes, when it gets dark – no flying,
If you don't mind. I'd rather take the train
So it might take a day or two. You're crying?
Oh don't, dear mum! It's only *west* Ukraine…"
But Readers, were those tears sprung less from grief
Than from a sense of unforeseen relief?

Then quickly travel plans were made. The Eurostar
Is cramped and overstuffed in standard seats –
The headrests itch and piped coloraturas jar
The fragile ear with recommended treats
In several tinny tongues, all oddly stressed
By buffet crewmen, faceless, dispossessed.

So: first class travel *tout droit* from St Pancras
To grubby Gare du Nord and all its odours
Of melting-butter-fat and pigeon cankers;
Then through the land where *bof* is *à la mode* as
The Champagne landscape plateaus: *Mittelrhein's*
Bright clouds emerge like froth from brimming steins.

The Hauptbahnhof in Köln will offer *wurst*
At every turn, and proud, officious staff
In red-trimmed navy uniforms that burst
With round, Kölsch-fattened paunches will all laugh
And twiddle with their facial topiary:
They're rarely helpful, but at least they're merry.

And then the *Jan Kiepura Nightline* sleeper
To Dortmund, Dusseldorf, Berlin then Poznań
(Or Posen to old Germans who would keep a
Possessive nomenclature) but because nine
Attendant hours elapse till their connection
They'll give the Kölner Dom's burnt husk inspection.

Their travails' last two legs I'll now relay
In more proximity: I hear them clatter
And clumsily adjust against the sway
Of wide-gauge Soviet rails. Their baggage matter
(Three plump Ikea bags in blue and gold)
Is stuffed within the under-couchette hold.

Their day shoes are exchanged for carpet slippers,
The windows opened up to welcome icicles
And frosted breath from Slavic gods (cloud-trippers
On iridescent silver wingéd tricycles,
Who watch on in amusement, giggling, winking,
Behind a carapace of stellar blinking).

The cold's incursion, strangely soporific
With pine-rich notes and undertones of sappiness,
Distils the carriage air. It folds pacific
Around the couple's transitory happiness.
They settle down to read beginners' guides
To foreign grammars, traffic laws and brides.

The nightlights in the corner of our cabins
Fade genially with the passing miles,
The ventilation grids waft out Scriabin's
Mazurka in F Major. Dreaming aisles
Outside each cosy six-foot-square enclosure
Extend and blur in sepia low-exposure:

A worming passage, dusky, never-ending,
With screeching coupling at its vertebrae;
A reek of burning rubber as each bending
Of muscle leans towards the coming day
With strained metallic cartilage. I'll doze,
And send my third eye out to flex its toes.

The landscape, hushed with buzzing night-flies, rests
In hunch-backed rolling knolls of snow-clad shivering;
The local fauna puffs its cheeks and breasts;
The dendral life, with wan, prolixious quivering,
Resists in vain the night sky's falling lather
As we pull through the limits of Warszawa.

Receding, Dworzec Centralny secretes
A sweat of seething breath and dead kebabs
And hums a rusty dirge of pock-marked streets,
Lost love in yellow wheat fields, taxicabs
And trams locked in electric, hateful clinches,
Extinct tradition, romance, beetroots, finches...

The sparkling spindles of the glum metropolis
Soon fade behind a sheet of throbbing fog –
The air is densely liquid and, on top of this,
Pollution thickens up the soup of smog –
The overall effect: a skein of candles
Deprived of oxygen by breathy vandals.

The last sky-scraping peak to meekly glimmer:
The proud Pałac Kultury, Stalin's "gift"
To underwhelmed Warszawa. Its thin shimmer
Spills down upon a squat poured-concrete nest
Of outbuildings and tramway tracks a-tangle
Within a bath of dimming neon spangle.

My electronic gecko roams the rugs
And lists with every maladroit sharp turn
But scuttles onward as our vessel chugs
And slaloms on. Its swivelled eyeballs burn
In alternating green and pillbox red
And whirring data spins within its head.

Let us go then, several coaches forward.
The cheaper, six-bunk class for impecunious
And hardy travellers: a toothless, poor herd
Of onion salesmen, livers wracked by ruinous
Tavarski vodka, stomachs roundly lined
By thick-sliced lard and gherkins fiercely brined.

Among them Wassily is inconspicuous.
He doesn't have the gut, but shares their cheekbones'
Pronouncement, noses' eastern arch, perspicuous
But frosted stare and snoring style: two bleak moans
(One inward, watery and intercostal,
One dry and outward) pass between each nostril.

Fat Tinky Winky slumbers safe beneath him.
A triple bolt (twelve-digit combination)
And fist-thick chain means no-one will relieve him
Of his weird baker's dozen. When a station
Slows into view his breathy sleep grows lighter
And anxious knuckles grip the handles tighter.

The bunk above him holds the bravely single,
Anomalously female budget fare:
A variegated wig of dirty shingle
Conceals her deeper mantle of dark hair.
She "sleeps" with one mistrustful eyelid cocked,
Her vital baggage, too, profoundly locked.

So far, so good enough. My clever players
Have all obeyed their deftly sculpted cues.
Wassily's feet rest safe beneath their layers
Of swaddle and await their earthen shoes
(In shallow sleep he pictures their descents
Into their thirteen pre-dug loamy dents).

As thankful as I am, though, I can't wallow
In gratitude's distracting, heavy swamp.
Our locomotion pulls, demands we follow
Its fuming forward march, its black-lung'd stomp:
The barb-wired eastern front of the EU
Is rapidly converging into view.

Ex-Soviet-style bloody-minded planning
Dictates that it's the middle of the night
When all our wheels screech still. The titan manning
The lunar spotlight pans from left to right;
Towards our cast, knee-deep in rising steam,
A squad of permafrosted jackboots stream.

SISSY

A gruff, torchlit incursion on the carriages
Ensues: passports are summarily snatched
From drowsy fingers, unconvincing "marriages"
Are queried with dark brows, hounds are dispatched
To verify with pulsing snubs' olfactory
Proficiency that all is satisfactory.

Of course, the border guards are in moustaches;
I count a cropped half-dozen variations:
The Ivan Franko Droop, The Golden Arches,
The Loaf of Bread, The Siamese Cetaceans,
The Bristling Dnieper Bridge, The Afghan Hound
(A facial Muybridge, frozen shaggy bound).

My buried self, the football commentator,
Now trembles as his buttocks set to squeaking.
The thick-necked pack of guards have made their way to
Wassily's bed. One brute, intent on peeking
Through Tinky Winky's phlox-hued, zippered pelt,
Should have his nosey collar sharply felt!

Lyudmila to the rescue: she emits
A siren-like, day-saving, yawn-cum-smile
That turns the rascal's head and thus acquits
The suitcase from a rough internal trial.
The meathead, with black eyes that threaten rape as
A perk of daily duty, belches "Papers!"

All over. Thankfully my friends in Streatham
Had done their usual job – they're very slick
But will extract the Michael if you let them.
(Don't pay for forging services on tick.
The interest charged is violent, astronomical,
And costs an arm and leg – not metaphorical.)

Distracted by a clamour three cars distal,
The burly stuffed potato turns upon
His military heel, burps out a mistral
Of *kiełbasa* (sausage) gas, is gone –
Drawn like an evil magnet to the bother
That's swollen round our hero and his mother.

The problem: there's one passport but two travellers.
It seems that Mother didn't have the forethought
(Indeed, she never saw this scene unravel as
Half plausible, though wishes now that more thought
Had been devoted to this grim scenario).
It's time to play the gallant impresario!

Five hulks, their heads and jaws all palely cuneiform,
Will not be budged – they smell an opportunity
For Western cash. I don my general's uniform
And sidle in. "This pair pass with immunity,
Or else..." (I pause to swell my intervention's
Bold gravitas) "You'll never smell your pensions!"

I wish the pair the very best vacation
And bid them welcome to Ukraine's rich soil,
Ensure them that their sense of trepidation
Should henceforth dissipate. No-one will spoil
Their rolling picaresque (and if they do,
They'll have me, personally, to answer to).

Then some advice best heeded in futurity:
"When offspring reach a lively upright state,
Can talk and earn (main trappings of maturity),
Can legally enlist or copulate,
An individual passport, adult-sized,
Would leave you – and your son – less compromised."

Some mumbled thankyous, dzatkujays, spaseebas,
An exhalation of exhausted breath,
The pair click off the light. Two damp amoebas
Who, half-aghast at having cheated death,
Combine as one: the usual drill ensues –
She spreads her skirts, he fumbles off his shoes.

I leave, my golden loafers softly strobing.
My ample army hems – horsehair galoshes –
Enshroud their auric glow in fusty robing
Like ankle-swinging, carpet-sniffing cloches.
Outside, the chilling dawn-grey light impinges
On black, and pulls night's trapdoor from its hinges.

My bed awaits, my couchette's rosy airs
Will wrap my head in gold but short-lived slumbering.
I dream of Warsaw's friendly cubs and bears✒
Entangled in their baby-oiled, dark rhumbaing,
The tango of their glossal-piercings' flicker
And conga-lines through tunnels smeared with liquor.

✒ For forty winks I'll leave thoughts of tomorrow
Deferred while I recall last night's excursions.
My evening's rounds began in *Toro Toro*
With Lech and Jan (two nominal "Cistercians" –
Both thoroughly observant, in their way,
Of all creation's wonders, bright and gay).

We sipped *Coquette* served in an iced tureen,
From twelve-inch Franz von Bayros vodka beakers
And watched through portholes from our mezzanine
As bacchanalia spread out beneath us
(As an aperitif, a great lip-wetter
Before your feast, it's hard to do much better).

We left the club and ventured further east:
The double-decker Gdański bridge, the Vistula –
A sordid Cocytus of foaming yeast –
To Praga, Warsaw's no-go-ville: a fistula
That leaks a fractious sap to terra firma
Through concrete layers that form the district's derma.

We walked (or rather *I* walked, my two queens
Minced feverishly with hydraulic swagger)
Through moss-lined alleyways, past dank shebeens,
Past Goths as thin as Macbeth's bloody dagger,
Then up a rusted carousel of stairs
To where we kept appointment with the bears.

Klub Saturator: gilded drawbridge, walls
Lined fresco-style in pop-up PVC,
A phallus striplamp (two smooth disco balls),
Framed Tom of Finland prints, free PCP
In every glass of *Smirnoff Black* and grapefruit,
Refulgent canapés of rose and snakeroot.

The fun began immediately: Lech
Shot straight for an acquaintance, plump, hirsute,
His chest an Afghan carpet, studded neck
Leashed tight above his handsome birthday suit.
Myself and Jan were beckoned to recline
On silk chaises longues and drink the visual wine.

The show – I shan't elaborate at length,
Distractions leave my recall under audit –
Was both a merry chase and test of strength.
Both showmen danced the grizzled *poète maudit*,
The *lucha libre* dwarf, and both took turns
And gifting in extremis Chinese burns.

The fun is always, I find, in the spooling
Of living frames across the gelid gaze;
While outwardly serene, within I'm drooling,
My synapses red-raw. Gauche passion plays
Are fun domestically (on DVD)
But pale compared with live-flesh verity.

The love-fight flowed, the wrestling trance continued;
Limbs rent asunder, bent, rent back again.
The bear was corpulent as Lech was sinewed:
A ball of woollen fat, a slender chain,
Thrashed wild between the walls of pimpled latex –
Lech peeling layers, revealing swollen Playtex.

Before too long a baying crowd had gathered
And formed a ring of tattooed flesh linked tight
In oily expectation. Pierced tongues slathered
And frothed beneath the spinning disco light.
Then soon, en masse, the human hula hoop
Set spinning in a crazed priapic loop.

The DJ raised the heat. The sonic weather
Grew *jouissant* and humid as Lou Reed
Drawled druggily of shiny boots of leather
Which thus provoked the dizzy centipede
To unlink throbbing parts and send them slipping
And sliding in a chorus of unzipping.

To join *the mise en scene's* excited middle
Was tempting, but, a voyeur soul at heart,
I bade young Jan step in as second fiddle
To daddy bear's strong-armed conductive art.
Besides, I felt a pang of absence flutter
And spread through me like melting wistful butter.

No Magda – as the underswell of dubstep's
Subsonic bass attacked the bones and plasma
I wished that she had clambered up the club's steps
And joined me in this glittering miasma.
She'd had her reasons, though – her concentration
Could not be coaxed from deep, chaste preparation.

And so I watched: a pile of leather jeans
With belt and buckle garnish soon amassed
And like from glossy skins of magazines
Its surface caught the strobe stream as it plashed
And sent it back in swerved refracted rays
To meet the glitter ball's Tiresian gaze.

A whale of manly body parts formed, sweating
A squall of salt towards the sky of rubber.
Some roughhouse fins lashed wild and hot blood-letting
Began around the softer spots of blubber
(Still to this day a sniff of *Smirnoff Black*
Recalls a hoary, spiral-nail-gouged back).

The ball grew taught and bellicose with glee.
My Lech and Jan were somewhere at the core
But far from desperate to erupt and flee
From deep within the pulsing humidor –
Hours later, quaffing through a chilled consignment
Of *Bols*, I learnt they got off on confinement.

I learnt a lot of other things in Praga,
Which, had I both the energy and line space,
I'd happily relate. But hark! The raga
Of dawn-grebes sounds! The fields are thatched with fine lace
Of milkweed, dew and fertilizer fluids,
And stalked by squads of white-clad scarecrow-druids.

Now we can see that Breeze Block Lane is festering
Beneath a spongiform caress of smog;
The bins aflame, the gutters full, and pestering
The panicked Boss (that's Neno's red-eyed dog)
Are rats of an outrageous, equine size:
I count a triple dozen pairs of eyes,

And half as many whip-like, ferrous tails,
Ejaculating snouts, a sea of whiskers
That cut as sharp as diamond. One impales
The maudlin hound's left oculus – his whimpers
Ring out in a traumatic fibrillation
Across Red Lanes and Whitefriars metro station.

And Neno recognises this strained whelp.
He knows its pliant frequency of hope.
He wishes he could offer human help
To canine need. But can't – he's bound in rope.
A rugged knot ensnares him to a chair.
His mouth is gagged. His gang: not anywhere.

Not anywhere too local, that is. But
They gather on Trafalgar Green and heat
Their satisfied gloved hands around a scut
Of barbequed toy horse. "We're near complete."
Says Jeb to Ham and Daniel. Neno Brown
Is too tied up to dominate this town!"

Oh dear. Oh dear. Oh dear. Oh dear. Poor Neno.
His troika are revolting. Coups round here
Come wrapped in bloody bows (think Tarantino,
Think Stealers Wheel, think Mr Blonde, think ear...)
So Neno sits as impotent as Attis
As Boss's rib's become a claret lattice.

And Neno's own lung-casement is *niezdrowy*
("Unhealthy") as his tremulous heart's beating
Contorts his rack. *Sub sole nihil novi
Est* on Second Earth though – power is fleeting
And any baron has to watch his back or
He'll end up compromised through front and back door.

Around the base of his four-legged jail,
A steady drip-drip-drip of fluid grows
To form a bodybag-shaped pool (the pail
Designed to catch his leakage overflows;
Its contents an invidious thick soup
Of lumpy dark maroon and plasmic goop).

Could there be but the slightest far-fetched hope
That somebody might save him from this ordure?
Whose porno nails might grapple with the rope
That binds him to his loathsome mortal torture?
His reinstated wife, the tattooed Beth,
Is all that stands between him and his death.

She rides a shark-drawn cab across the Thames,
Alerted by the Doberman's limp squealing.
Its tone, resigned and drained, she knows condemns
Poor Boss to canine hell, where every ceiling
Is hung with dripping bones just out of reach
And vengeful postmen wield a studded leash.

Although disheartened, she knows Neno Brown
Must be in danger. Jumping to the shore
By Sodom Bridge's pinions she flags down
Another cab – this one propelled by boar –
And hurtles to the bunker where she fears
Her husband waits in deafened hope (*sans* ears).

Beth skids round hairpin corners, bosom rattling
Her T-bone corset, platinum-blonde mane
Athwart the night like fronds of lightning battling
A cinerous phalange of latent rain.
She hurtles wildly onward on her journey
To Neno, to preserve him from the gurney.

So, all change! Disembark for our denouement
In verdant countryside amid the flocks
Of proud unwitting extras (their procurement –
A pile of Levi's 501s, a box
Of Marlboros, iPhone5s and an array
Of fragrances from Ghost and Gaultier).

But first, as Lemberg/Lviv/Lwów's outer orbit
Of concrete, tattooed brick and cobblestone
(Piled high with iced slush piles of lemon sorbet
Dropped earthward from a deity's spent cone)
Pulls into gaunt relief, I roll, lick, spark
A coarse, lung-lacerating pinch of Lark.❟

❟ These days I seldom smoke: a hypnotherapist
  In Wembley waved her spangled rubber arms
  And with conviction deep as any terrorist
  Intent on self-erasure worked her charms.
  The blanket ban has one loophole: Ukraine,
  In transit, most especially the train.

I watch through blue-grey plumes as Geckocam™
Shows crusty-lidded Wassily now stirring –
Still hugging Tinky Winky's diaphragm –
And mum and Sissy dressing (mother shirring
A Kom-Fut babcia headscarf round her ears
With fingers needle-sharp, eight-knuckled spears).

Here's Magda at her busy, fragrant toilette.
New eyebrows, lashes, lenses, beauty-spot
(A fragile job, she's careful not to spoil it
And give her pale crêpe cheeks a streaming blot),
Resaturation of her flaming mane,
So here we have Lyudmila back again.

And now we reach Lviv station, grand but dated.
Its dome a giant silver-skinned balloon
Of gleaming *łuski* ("wooski", scales), steel-plated
And proud beneath the double-beams of moon
And sun. A limestone Hypnos, drowsy, solemn,
Glares trackwards from his lofty Toscan column

And surveys with his weary *oczy* (eyes)
Our stretching characters as they vacate
The train's blue hull and reacclimatise
To non-vibrating ground. The upright state
Invokes a minor vertigo between their
Wide pupils in the sudden rush of clean air.

Sissy drags their stuffed holdalls of chattels
Across the concourse (freshly mopped and gleaming
It re-reflects the glassy roof). Mum rattles
Behind him, overflowing pockets streaming
With crushed umbilicals of tissue paper,
Her every pore emitting anxious vapour.

Her thoughts run thus, "I soon to meet my daughter,
Or daughter-in-the-law. How wracked my nerves!
How trembling shakes my body's every quarter!
Oh how I hope she thoroughly deserves
My little Sissy's innocent, plump hand!"
But hunger interrupts ("A sausage stand!")

The two engorge themselves on *kabanosy*,
Parówki, tasteless white and yellow cheeses,
Burnt *kawa rozpuszaczlna* (instant coffee)
And stolid rye bread rolls. Lyudmila seizes
Her window of free undetected flight
And glides unhurriedly beyond their sight.

Myself, I stand within the regal booking hall
And watch beneath the swirls of art nouveau
And internet-for-rent. (I can't help looking: all
The teenage boys – an acned, bird-backed row,
Like crows on overhanging country cables –
Glare hunched at porno, hands beneath their tables

In one almighty fidget; girls, blonde-headed
And rosy-cheeked spray dust-soaked Basra alleys
From graphic Humvees; youngsters slay the dreaded
Louche flesh of Carmen Sandiego.) Sallies
Of scrofulous black swifts dart from the eaves
And loop the hall in flapping semibreves.

In all, a fitting welcome for young Wassily,
Who, as I speak, is dragging his companion's
Low centre of plum, adipose, packed gravity
Through centre stage. His fingers, like the banyan's
Dense roots still grasp his booty with a fervour
Of fear and mild relief there's not much further.

He stops to buy a chewy smoked *kabanos*
And chomps it with one hand. His neighbours' habits
Raise eyebrows: their combined consumptive *telos*
Is not to merely satiate. Like rabbits
Who breed until the slope flies off the axis
Of birth-rate graphs, theirs is an endless praxis

Of stuffing, moistening and mastication;
A brief impasse for freight to pass between
Their bloated gates of fervent gurgitation
And ventric acid-baths that strip bones clean
Of fleshy sustenance, and then resumption
Of feeding with renewed, redoubled gumption.

But then the pull of transit tugs: the hour
To board a rusted decommissioned coach
And thud through lanes roofed thick with rowan bower
Is drawing near. They let their stomachs poach
Their sausage into fatty faecal thickets
And shuffle roundly off to buy their tickets

For fair Lyudmila's distant rural locus.
Wassily, undelighted, realises
He's in their gaseous slipstream. In his focus:
Two sweat-stained backs in two inflated sizes
(XXL and XXXXL)
Both rippling with an oily underswell.

Here, Sissy, now inspired by his old phrasebook
Attempts a base transaction: nothing doing.
The ticket-madam's face, her blunt, unfazed look,
Which hints at something slow and violent brewing
Beneath its sheen of macerated gum,
Unmans him. He retreats behind Fort Mum.

In rusty half-Ukrainian she steps up
And finds the right gruff timbre – part guffaw,
Part brace of stabbing sibilants – that sets up
A shrill interrogation as each floor
Of intonation's glassy tower is climbed
In bounding polysyllables (half-rhymed);

Then with a glacial half-nod she takes hold
Of *bilety* and quaking son and joins
The queue of flat-capped peasants by the mould-
Encrusted *Bogdan Bus.* Wassily's coins
Pursue her rusting hrivna and soon land
In ticket madam's grey and palsied hand.

Behind them in the queue with Tinky Winky
He twitches his affronted nose in wrinkles
Of maddened pink. What is this *fetor* (stink) he
Seems fated not to shake? Why must these sprinkles
Of salted human coolant fly towards him?
Is this how god's soft watchfulness rewards him?

The local stares, the vocal English bafflement,
The slightly more expensive clothes, the *size* of them;
All this attacks the anxious mental battlement
That Wassily has built. He evil eyes at them
To silently communicate: "Please rest
Unnoticed, do not faff and fuss, my quest

May not be jeopardised by your ridiculous,
Shrill nasal jabbering (one part drained estuary
And one part numbed Slavonic); your conspicuous
Synthetic branded goods, the blinking bestiary
Of slim and bleeping gewgaws and machines,
Their tinny jabbering and livid screens…"

Here Sissy's sweating, *różowe, pyzate*
i skarłowaciałe palce ("stunted
And fat pink fingers"), each a stuffed skin-patty
Of high-fat dough, glide wet on the chrome-fronted
Nintendo 3DS that he's extracted
From somewhere... high-speed chases are enacted

Round Venice Beach, St Petersburg and Rio
In various fat, hyperreal cars:
A six-wheeled hearse, a souped-up Renault Clio
With razor-blade encrusted bully bars.
His mother fiddles with a gadget too –
An iPad – as she watches *Wrong Turn2.*

Our driver is phlegmatic and nonplussed –
The only sign of fluster is his reaching
For vodka from his hip flask. Clouds of dust
Fly up around our bus, which lists right, beaching
Uncomfortably on hedgerows deep with prickle:
The driver liberates us with his sickle...

...and off we are. Another stilling swig
And everything churns forward once again.
The dust has settled. Piles of leaf and twig
Lie trembling in their numb organic pain
And wreath a watching peasant and his horse
In winding sheets of juniper and gorse.

Our western visitors are in cold sweats.
They drop their handheld comforts to the floor
And hold each other's hands. Wassily lets
Things pass him by. He's seen it all before.
Lyudmila, in a *matryoshka* shroud
Of layered scarf/disguise exclaims out loud

In broad, trucker-Ukrainian, "You fool!
Oovaha! Boževilnij! Pay attention!
Where did you learn to drive? The special school
For fat, *debilni* (backward) kids?" The tension
Is broken by the driver's mate, who passes
Round mollifying schnapps in plastic glasses.

We're slowly closing space between ourselves
And where we need to be, past km markers
In swift descent (worn 50s, rusty 12s,
A faded 9) and then we hit our mark as
We reach a milestone town (a crumbling chapel,
A spastic tree with one surviving apple),

Then kilometres on the roadside signs
Spin up in number like on fruit machines
Whose cherry pairs and spangled dollar-vines
Revolve in promise. Then the road careens
In front of us, a threshing tail of clay
That splits in half the flat-ironed, endless day.

Our destination, will we ever reach it?
Or will we, like an arrow shot by Xeno
Encroach against a gap but never breach it,
Forever doomed by sophistry's casino
To watch the wheel spin round its reds and blacks
Eternally down ever-circling tracks?

This anxiousness is daft, my thoughts will clear
Once I have shut my lids' fatiguing peel
And spent an hour or two in Bedfordshire.
I'm bound to wake with goal in sight and feel
Jak nowonarodzony (freshly born)
And shot of worry's titillating thorn.

So now I'll sleep. This Hellenistic doubting
Will dissipate amid my dreams of tendons
All flexing up thin calves, toes gamely sprouting
From alabaster insteps, painted chevrons
On nacreous, buffed nails. I'll re-emerge,
Smooth-skinned, sleep-charged upon our final verge.

Around that corner what will be in view?
A disparate array of Flackboard shacks,
A sesquipedal donkey and my crew
Of hirelings: uncle Vlad (face lined with cracks
As deep as Lake Baikal), the cousins Popov
All interchangeable, each with a crop of

Albino feathers spinning round their crowns,
Nadezhda Filipovna in her get-up
Of last year's Маркс і Спенсерс modish browns –
Her skirt, a grim velour, split high to let up
A louche convection wave of thinning air
And proudly flaunt her Гуччі underwear.

Ivan Demenchonok will greet us smiling
With all his three impacted teeth and lift
His furball fox-felt hat (the iron filing
Beneath pricked up, an agitated drift
Of overwhelmed and hyperactive static)
Then offer bear hugs, Slavic and emphatic,

To bid us "Welcome to my proud *osada*,
Where goats are goats and men are more than men;
Where women glow with sweetly rustic ardour;
Whence many left and few came back again.
The sausages are prime, the gin primordial
(Especially when mixed with bosen cordial)."

One eye, one ear, one flappy tongue between them,
The Popov trio (Hanka, Anka, Vanka)
Flank Mother in a whirling mohair screen then
Convey, at length, that they would like to thank her
For offering her only son's rich hand
To wear a modest local wedding band.

They then (at further muddled length) convince her
That custom here dictates she is removed
To various ablutions: they will rinse her
Corporeally, scrub her till she's smoothed
Of every whorling barnacle, each bump
Of excess *skóra* (skin), each oily sump

Within her many central folds will sluice
Towards a gilded bucket with the aid of
A poultice, brume-brush, swabs of beetroot juice
And finger tips. The masque the city's made of
Her dermis will flake off, the urban venom her
Tubes clog with will be flushed with purging enema.

And though her origins are roughly local,
Our girl capitulates ("*Dziwaczny* (quaint)
These rustic ways!") recalling anecdotal
Reports from childhood (roosters balmed in paint
And hurled on burning haystacks, wildcat bacon
Served up on namesdays), lets herself be taken

As willing prisoner across a threshold
Of plaited garlic skin and flickering bunting,
And in, through corridors of lambent mesh, gold
Brocaded handrails, pen-and-inks affronting
Even my own loose concept of propriety
Such is their candid, colourful variety...

Until, securely bundled from our scene
(And any danger of a fraught, maternally-
Charged *interwencja* gone) her captors clean
And lube her flanks both inter and externally.
Nadezdha Filipovna, lips a-pucker,
Waits by the coach to offer Sissy succour.

Indeed, our hero is in need of warming.
He shivers in an existential whirl
Of nervous, clammy doubt. His jowls are forming
Their standard maudlin droop, his fingers curl
In troubled clamps around his purpling thumbs
And puppy dogteeth pinch at frigid gums.

She takes him under one plump, buttered wing,
Its plumage perfumed bitterly. This haptically
Effusive clinch inspires his pores to sting,
His flesh to ripple slowly yet emphatically,
But then the loamy noxiousness embalms him,
A wave of Шанель номер п'ять becalms him.

Now Uncle Vlad impales his other flank
With salad-fingered, mucus-dribbling talons,
And Sissy's legs, each one a deadened shank
Of Arctic clay, drag limp through pre-churned gallons
Of *osad* (sludge) and *bagno* (mud) like Twiglets
Through satay sauce. A bilge-caked swarm of piglets

(A grunting roadblock) scatter as Vlad's toes
Reach outward with a prodding malefaction;
A funerary flutter of gaunt crows
Obscure the late sun's rays in dark diffraction:
Our human, arm-linked triptych now retreats
Down pathways neatly lined with early beets.

So. Mother: indisposed. Her son: the same.
We will return to them anon. But wait!
Wassily, like a lapping bush-fire flame,
Has seared across the fields with lightening gait.
(Now even Tinky Winky's freight can't slacken
His fervid progress over moss and bracken.)

My General Custer costume[✎] (and my self,
Its rippling and amorphic limbs and senses
Within the khaki cloth) pursue – an elf
With nimble, Pan-like bounds. I scale sharp fences,
Leap bleeding rivulets, climb greasy peaks,
Dodge treacherous, low-flying egret beaks...

——————————

[✎] At times like this the elements compel me
To change like a capricious lepidoptera
And find another costume to en-shell me
In limpid new relief: one-legged doctor or
Starved, cross-eyed bigamist who trades in cartons?
Pale, pre-op acolyte of Dolly Parton's?

The purple fridge and scrawny sprite keep flying
Pulled by a sphery lodestar through a clew
Of darkling thorns, Wassily's thumbs untying
The piquant skein to let his baggage through,
And onward, as the dusk's wild-toned orison
Descends, they strike out over the horizon.

I keep my watchful distance in a tunnel
Of pricked-up samphire grass. Out comes the reptile.
I pierce the rump-port, click a switch and funnel
A pint of battery fluid in. The sectile,
Crisp Woodchip flies up wildly in its wake –
A whirlwind cloud of frozen downy flake.

Soon up to speed with Wassily, its quarry,
The Geckocam™ records his bounds and jumps:
More stiles are skipped, crushed twigs (*mementi mori*
To poestastic souls) snap, burnt-out stumps,
Each marked with arcane tatuage, provide him
With fey co-ordination. Deep inside him

Half-deaf solicitor, green briefcase weighted
With rare injunctions (super, gold and über)?
Young Windsor, incognito, latex-pated
And potty-mouthed? Frostbitten lost Yoruba?
Or well-shaved panda (dress-suit, double-breasted)?
These all are options, each rehearsed and tested

But not the thing I'm after on this blustery,
Potato-coloured morning. I'll transform thus:
Blue, silver-buttoned coat (a General Custery,
Thick, epaulletted, martial thing) a formless
Flat hat with drooping peak, and cream plus fours:
Ideal attire for *Kresy's* bog-strewn moors.

His atavistic blood-sense sends its messages
To every trilling cell: you're getting closer,
You're *prawie* (nearly) there. This fervour presages
A cataract of sweat. A racemosa
Of glands engorge his neck, his breast, his loins;
His eyes dilate (less pearls, more burnished coins)

Until, *tak nagle* (suddenly) he stops.
He checks the wind with wetted middle fingers:
A starchy breeze from late potato crops
Wafts round his flooded temples and malingers
Like soup-scent fuming from a milk bar's doorway
In gusts of ice as cold as western Norway.

"This is the hallowed spot!" he cries aloud
To Tinky Winky, who remains unmoved
Until he is unzipped. A greyscale cloud
Evaporates. The sky, now microgrooved
With ashen stretch-marks, wrinkles out above them –
Then dark descends to spectrally englove them.

The gecko, on a smooth strategic branch,
Feeds back in infra-red. Its guzzling zoom
Dilating like a voyeur's with carte blanche
On fifty peepholes to a changing room
Of netball nymphets wrapped in frilly trim,
Though on my screen there is no pre-starched gym.

From my embedded spot, upon my palmtop:
The thirteen feet step earthward from their casement
Like hunks of meat in transit from some farm shop
Of gory cuts. Their delicate emplacement
In catafalques of clay will soon ensue
But Wassily first has some work to do.

With telescopic spade and whalebone trowel
He digs the L-shaped trenches, then he lines them.
Each one receives a pre-cut bathing towel
And gold thread monogram that thus defines them
As Maxim or Sławomir, Ctik, Bronislaw,
Mieczyslaw, Teofil, Lech, or Stanislaw.

He takes a little breath, then Alyosha's
Toes lower into place, are swamped in layers
Of soil with two encouraging galoshes.
Then finally Zbigniew, Tadeusz,
Ezekiel and Leopold complete
The trench of cold repatriated feet.

Now Geckocam™ pans out. In bas-relief
Our gravedigger lies slumped against the soil.
The lunar spotlight burns on tears of grief-
Cum-joy and brings his eyelids to the boil
Like salinated crucibles. Half-sightless
They wince beneath a sudden flood of whiteness.

The lizard's eye enlists its snow-proof blades
Which flick half mechanistic, half organic
And clear the lens each time its vision fades.
The zinc dust makes the earth glow epiphanic
As now the sky explodes. Through dream clouds pour a
Thick caravan of stars in bright aurora.

And what is this? From in between gnarled branches
The lens picks up a rising row of gables
Protruding through the backdrop's snow-thick tranches
And growing as if pulled by spectral cables
All splaying moonwards in an arched palmetto
Strummed keenly by a twinkly-eyed Geppetto.

The *Dom Tańczący's* conic roof now forms.
Around it incandescent souls find shape.
Girls scatter in a centrifugal swarms
Of dervish arms and legs. A glowing cape
Of stars and ectoplasm twines around them.
Then thirteen re-emergent boys surround them.

A pair unites: an octopedal burka
Of coruscating light and silver skin.
And lo! From in the trees a fierce mazurka
Compels their lucent orbits to begin.
They weave through willow tendrils, pirouetting
And swooning in a rash of undead petting.

Oh! How they move in artful pandemonium
To airborne instruments – a wingéd lute,
A flapping contrabass, a gold harmonium
And floating plump accordion; their fruits
Drop down upon the fizzing soil and swatch its
Soft carpet in a flood of gleaming crotchets.

The rest conjoin as well. Each Pan with Panna,
Each Ruslan with his revenant Lyudmila,
Each Eugene finds his freshly-lithe Tatiana,
Each Zombie finds his Zombiette. A *Thriller*-
Style flashdance now breaks out across the ice
And stubbled earth. I feel like Vincent Price!

Mazurka shifts to waltz, to jive, to mambo,
Then slow jam as the couples merge still tighter
And one, two, three, pop! Thirteen human flambeaux
Ignited by an otherworldly lighter
Explode – each one a shorted orgone box
Of energy. What's left: a bed of phlox.

BEN BOREK

The spinning set, lights dimmed, now hums pacifically.
The chorus is subdued; the central members
Now rest, mid-pose, like tokens hieroglyphically
Engraved on tundra glazed with hissing embers.
The trees all shrug their many aching angles
(Despite an evening's dance, still knotted tangles).

And what of Wassily throughout this *Son
Et Lumiere* show? Fast asleep, and phthisically
He breathes like a depleted Oberon
Within a woodland respite home for physically
Exhausted souls whose life's work, now achieved,
Has left them self-reflexively bereaved.

The time has now arrived to let the fader
Engulf the scene in my director's cloud
And pull the rolling credits' moonlit veda,
So camera newts and gaffer geckos shroud
The dwindling film. Last shot: In one dark corner
There sits a hunched, black taffeta'd old mourner.

No. Aunt Svetlana cannot jubilate.*
The magic *übermenschen* and their girls
May well have found their peace but her long wait
For closure has not ended. Grief unfurls
In crystal ribbons from her withered sockets
And other orifices, holes and pockets.

----

* *O biada mi! Gdzie jest mój ładny syn?*
   (Where is my handsome son? Oh woe is me!)
   Her gurn is so contorted that a grin
   Of bitter sickled lips spreads desperately
   Across a leather century of dents
   And wrinkles, sadnesses and discontents.

And here the very last sad credits cut:
There's Tinky Winky, vacuated, dead,
His role fulfilled, he's now a hollowed nut
Of lavender. His zippers bust, his head
Serrated to reveal a scarified
Equator, thorned stigmata pock his hide.

While others wandered withered but heroic
The hamlet's fourteenth (later-hatching) youth
(A knock-kneed bantam, red-eyed, cryptozoic)
Was stuck like an unseen impacted tooth
To fester in its cavity and wallow
Undecorated in this backwood hollow.

He kept the charcoal heating systems burning,
Birthed, mucked out, slaughtered, minced up all the swine.
In martial flux, the world around him turning
Its maddening lasso of plosive twine
(Each loop more ruthless, each rough twist of thread
More caked in blood), he kept the chickens fed.

A thousand harrowed nights of this he strained,
Unloved, unnoticed, selflessly maintaining
A *mode de vie* for those that still remained
And those who one day might be re-remaining,
Till, one grim day, just as Svetlana feared,
Her son was bundled up and disappeared.

What next? She doesn't even want to know.
The guesswork would mean gruesome flights of fancy.
But what is sure as *nieszczęście* means woe:
No act of weird benignant necromancy
Transported him to Wroxham, Hove or Ely,
Or any place where breath would greet him freely.

So she'll stay wreathed in black in perpetuity
As all of the ex-static souls around her
Take deep contented root. No cashed annuity
Of settled moral solace will impound her
Deep treacle-dark black dog within a kennel
Of post-death rest beneath the ferns and fennel.

Let's browse the Shanxi snaps my trusted gecko's
Unflagging eye recorded for posterity:
I flick back through – the first, *après* El Greco's
Laocoön attacked by serpent ferity,
Has Sissy on his naked back resisting
A skein of grubby overzealous fisting.

The second, more suggestive of a Bacon,
Reveals his mouth extending from his shoulders,
A frozen rictus, mute and godforsaken,
As those same fists, unwieldy knuckled boulders,
"Massage" his tense pre-nuptual skin (an honour
Reserved for grooms and oiled with belladonna).

Shot number three has Sissy on a table,
Spreadeagled like a hog in marinade.
A spikey box of tools loaned from the stable
Throbs rustily, preparing to invade.
I think of Rembrandt's operating theatre
With Dr Tulp above his cold pieta.

The fourth, a blurry Tillmanns: Sissy's chained
Against a wall flash-flooded white, thin windings
Of grout between the brick squint out. His reined
Abraded limbs tug limp against their bindings
Of dark corrosive lead and toxic nickel.
His splitting spine describes a fattened sickle.

The final shot, crepuscular and grainy,
Depicts a boy on sheets stained plum and mustard.
Dawn's breaking yellow fingers, chapped and veiny,
Spill over him like streams of toxic custard.
Above him stands the panting coalition
Of souls who form his welcoming commission.

The window through which morning bleeds (an oriel,
Crosshatched with wires) affords a mangled view
Of craning necks both human and arboreal.
A pair of eyes intensely glaucous blue
Look inward from beneath their lust-red brows
(The left, amused, arcs, mimicking the boughs).

Lyudmila, straining ivory phalanges
And – oh my! – perfect naked heels – excuse me! –
Dark muscle flowing upward like two Ganges
Of flawless sheeny sinew... how this moves me
To lacrimate a little for the joy: a
Bliss-filtered tributary from *River Voyeur*!

She meets the wrinkled gaze on the divan
And bats her scandalously dripping lashes.
Numb recognition hits his brain ("But can
That really be...?") before it melts and crashes,
His hard-drives overworked, his boiling RAM
Infested with his psychosexual spam.

The smile that rattled memory's slant door meant
One thing: he sensed it vaguely but profoundly.
His pounding ceremonials of torment
Had just begun. He slept, though far from soundly.
This time descriptions won't be entered into
Of what his dreams were. It would feel a sin to.

On sumptuous feet, away Lyudmila trots.
I feel thanks more than words to my brave lizard
For swivelling to grab some landscape shots.
These must be framed. They will be wrapped in izard.
They will be blown up huge and trailed from biplanes
To quell both Peckham riots and crippling migraines.

But forward to the wedding ring:✒ brown smog
Has risen from a wormhole in the frost
To lick like some cadaverous wet dog
At merrymaking calf fat and accost
Unpadded knees, uninsulated glutes,
Unstockinged halluxes beneath their boots.

✒ I've touched already on the films of Wajda
(The Gielgud dubbing weirdness, you'll recall)
To take my oeuvre-view a little wider
Let's watch *Wesele*. It's a wedding ball.
"Young Poland" (*Młoda Polska*) will unite
Across the social veils. For one drunk night.

It brings to celluloid a work of theatre
By Stanisław Wyspiański (painter-poet).
Set circa 1900. Poland, near to
Integrity, flushed proud. How best to show it?
Among the classes bookish and artistic
The trend was: celebrate the atavistic.

A country barn is full of intellectuals
Fat journalists, thin poets (one's the groom –
A scrawny wispy beard in oval spectacles
Whose beady peppercorns survey the room,
Its central dancing-pit and dim periphery,
That hosts symposia on goat midwifery).

The bride's a local girl in folky garb:
Voluminously crinkled linen blouse,
Embroidered swishing skirts, a glinting barb
Of rustic light bulbs bright beneath thick brows.
And here's the point – he loves this opposition.
He's actively betrothing folk tradition.

He didn't want his proud bloodstream injected with
The Austro-flavoured kiss of Kraków women.
For him this matrimony reconnected with
The old folkloric *real*. This need to swim in
The simple past was order of the day.
1901: Nostalgia was *au fait*.

So round the room the camera span its rope.
It stopped to eavesdrop over disquisitions
On homeland politics and future hope,
Among both living souls and apparitions
Of hetmen, phantoms, pierrots, bearded knights,
And *chochoły* (clumps of hay that haunt the nights).

The film achieves a giddy blurred crescendo:
Vainglory of a drunken call to arms
That quickly fades to fogged diminuendo
As some poor fool with sweaty nervous palms
Thuds through the frozen barn. Each static pawn
Awaits the sound of his lost golden horn:

But as it is as lost as one's virginity
Post gangbang (and for this I blame the *chochoł*)
The players congregate in the vicinity;
The mist-filled landscape clinches tight to scotch all
Attempts at some neat ending, meteopathic
And clear. Instead they swirl as waltzing traffic.

Let us now freeze that frosted scene, dear Readers.
For more description buy yourselves the feature.
I've glossed over a lot (the crazed stampede as
They arm themselves with spears, the warty creature –
Some sort of diabolic Slavic jester
With skin like mottled scarlet polyester...)

So, yes, a ring of wedding-goers clad in
Delightfully old-fashioned woven outfits.
The clouds waft round buff ankle boots (a fad in
The early century). Their polka outwits
The dimpled field and round they move, some blearily,
Some semi-comatose, others more cheerily.

Quite honestly, this was my motivation
For bringing up *Wesele* in this context.
It seems that Wajda's Kodachrome creation
Foresaw our current scene – two mystic gongs flexed
Across the space-time void and resonate
Both there and here in chiming duplicate.

BEN BOREK

Our hero,⟋ moderately vivified,
Spins round his head a full 360 circle
Like some despairing owl with eyes as wide
As wagon wheels. His teeth vibrate, limbs jerk all
Directions and yet somehow he stays planted
On one foul spot, more curséd than enchanted.

But where is mother? Sissy craves the solace
Of her safe womb, and tilts his wonky neck
(He has what doctors call a *torticollis*,
Produced by years of hunched-up sleep). From deck
To sky he scans for her maternal shape,
The globe that represents for him "escape".

⟋ Or almost duplicate – a vital difference:
The groom is now a dozen inches shortened
(That length has shifted to his stuffed circumference),
His eyes are deeper-sunk, his veins are tautened
By Burger King and *sel* (that's "sól" *gallice*)
And Credit Crunch for lunch. Yes, it is Sissy.

He cuts a traumatised and haunted shape
Amid the celebrants. His prolapsed chins
Are somewhere deep inside his quaking nape.
His knocking knees' sick timpani begins
A mortified calypso of damp bone.
He's never felt more vacant. Or alone.

What happened to him in the silage shed
Behind the beetroot fields beyond the bramble?
What dark abuse has palsied him with dread
That what occurred was just a light preamble
To further degradations, pain and pinching?
Why is his whole pink skin-suit taut with flinching?

But her absurdist waistline isn't there yet,
Among her son's new friends in fancy dress.
She's deep in consultation with a hair net
And pots of armpit polish. Her distress
Before a crumbling mirror's smashed mosaic,
When measured against his, is more prosaic.

"Girls, help me. I'm not chose. Which fascinator?
The *żółty* (gold) or *biały* (white)?" The Popovs
Confer. Hanka's grey eyeball pops its crater
Of wrinkle-flaps. She skewers it on top of
A toasting fork and waves it round mum's head.
Then Vanka's tongue lisps out *"czerwony"* (red).

The trio scuttle round with sheets of fabric
And drape their client's monstrous sweaty humps
In patterned linen, *Crêpe de Chine* and cambric.
Throughout this Anka mercilessly pumps
Mum full of Bison juice (bypassing lips
It enters through three handspun catgut drips).

This magic liquid, rich in THC
From local fungi, forest opiates,
And wormwood extract from the Bering sea
Has spread, since dusk, when first it passed the gates
Of mum's metabolism like a spider
Of sickly calm, and quelled all fear inside her.

She hasn't seen a single worried picture
Of Sissy on her superego's screen,
Where normally her thoughts, ruled by one stricture
('How is my son?'), would now be gelatine
And trembling with maternal apprehension,
Instead her neurons bob in warm suspension.

And cut: another boudoir, *plein de* powder
Less scatological, less like Swift's Celia's
Delightful fleshy *toilette*. Smoke rings cloud a
More *demi-mondaine* sexpot *aux camellias*
(But healthier, without the tragic cough)
In fits of trying on and taking off.

It is Lyudmila (there's as little doubt
Of this as of Orlando's opening gender).
She sucks her tiny middle, angles out
Already overhanging breasts to lend a
Rococo timbre to the silhouette
That wafts behind her pulsing cigarette.

It seems that she (good girl) is slowly settling
Upon an outfit cheap as it is garish.
A Poundland gown with nylon garters kettling
Protesting skin. Its shoulders (padded, squarish)
Provide a frilly altar for her skull –
A crinoline *bateau* with sharp-jawed hull.

She touches up her rouge, re-does the mole
That transit's wheels had faded into flesh.
Her fingers, with immaculate control,
Sew carefully within the *oczko* (mesh)
That trails from her tiara's plastic bones
Two pearls that double up as microphones.

Upon a barrow dais the Popovs wheel
The mother-of-the-sickening-young-groom,
Now gibbering and honking like a seal
Lobotomised and caked in fragrant spume.
They dump her in her place beside her boy.
She stretches out a palm. Their life-lines cloy.

And what a pretty picture they now make
United in disoriented trembling
(This echoes in the nine-tiered jelly cake
That has appeared stage left). Dry-mouthed, dissembling,
The child remarks upon the spread "Look, drumsticks
And party rings. They've shipped in Tizer!" Mum flicks

Her ochre eyelids down, her tongue's vermillion
Out perpendicular. Her scalene head
Lolls coldly back and forth, benumbed, reptilian.
From somewhere an accordion is bled
Of drones. The solid sky's thick slab of antimony
Reflects the minor notes of pending matrimony.

My tailored, all-terrain robes do their job
As now I stride across the wedding field.
The air hangs thick and rich with sautéed squab
But underfoot the *bagno* has congealed
To form (in varied browns) a glassy slate
Upon which I half tip-toe and half skate.

The lung of Vladimir's old cystic squeezebox
Now splutters out my priestly⟋ entry tune.
I *salco* to the alter (five stacked breeze blocks)
To strains of an asthmatic *Clair de Lune*
And bless the chairless crowd in minted spit
Then bid them: "squat my flock, best not to sit."

"Friends, gathered on this patch of frosted sod
In our resplendent ring of humankind,
Regard now the propitious sketch that god
Has scribbled on the canvas of his mind!
With holy pen and sacramental inking
He has designed two souls' eternal linking!

⟋ In Lviv, when you weren't looking, I absconded
And met my dexterous tailor Aleksander
(Sub rosa and sub-street, the trapdoor fronded
In camouflaging veils of oleander,
His office, like the Steppenwolf's, is *Not
For Everyone*). We talked. We had a shot

Or two of something wholesome and reviving.
Then *drank*. Here hospitality is measured
(First off, before one's waist) upon arriving
Within the anteroom – bedecked with treasured
And glinting threads – in golden centilitres.
(Once very drunk, talk moves to centimetres.)

I hope the prayer books have been passed around?"
(They have – the smudgy Xeroxed hymns all flutter
In shivering fingertips, tobacco-browned
And gloved up to the knuckle.) "Let me utter
My thanks. The bride is here. We must receive her,
But first, to all of you, dear guests: *spaseeba*.

We all are here assembled to bear witness:
Lyudmila, gentle daughter of this manor,
Blessed with rare Slavic Beauty, sunny fitness
Of limb and nature, countenance of manna
And luck of Tyche, travelled far and wide
(To Cricklewood), and now returned a bride.

And Sissy, waiting patient in the womb
Of Dulwich, shaded by the Peckham ferns
And nurtured in the City's waiting room
Of *Olde* lanes and follied glass. At turns
He felt *ennui* then *mauvaise fois*, but hope
Won out and chafed through solitude's dark rope.

    ———————

    The fitting scene I'll gloss across. If keenness
    To have a fuller picture must infect you
    To bridle at the well-constructed cleanness
    I jump from *thens* to *nows* with, I direct you
    To seek out chapter 3 of *Donjong Heights*
    For fuller-stitched sartorial delights.

    But what did I leave clutching from that nook?
    What raiment was now wrapped in tender tissue
    And lodged within my drunken elbow's crook?
    A flowing robe of sacerdotal issue
    With matching collarino, gloves and socks
    That Aleksander called 'nu-Orthodox'.

Let us now thank the miracle of *miłość*,
The gift of love's bright lottery, where tickets
Are punted on for kopeks in fate's kiosk
And hope crawls resolute through luckless thickets
Led on by Aphrodite's watchful drover
Like hardy sperm towards a distant ova.

Let's thank as well the kindly internet.
Within its webs of scam and vice one forum,
An island of goodwill, exists to let
Lost singletons unite in coupled quorum.
So though we thank our lord, our praise is greater
To Slavic Beauty's site administrator!

With that, dear comrades, join with me. Please stand.
Nadezhda Filipovna, prep your choir;
Vladimir, kindly prime your wedding band;
Ivan Demenchonok, ignite the fire;
Lyudmila is now ready to process.
We cannot have the frost bespoil her dress!"

And here she comes. The Popovs hold her train
Within their three gnarled pairs of hoary wicker.
Vladimir's wheezy band pipes up again.
A tealight runway guides her, wicks a-flicker,
Between an arch of withered, dripping pines
Encased in impotently frozen vines.

And lo! A chink within the ashen skyline
Breaks open. Sunlight pumps upon her frills
And rainbow ribbons meet her smiling eyeline.
It is as if the pullulating gills
Of some leviathan have flexed above
And offered us a breath of sunnied love.

She winks at Sissy (languorously shading
An opal orb beneath a fan of lash)
And pouts at mum (a nonchalant parading
Of jellied scarlet labia round a gash
Of wicked black) while slinking to the altar
Like some precocious leotarded vaulter.

And with no *matka* of the bride, nor father,
Nadezhda Filipovna fills both roles. Her
Fat hand hooks deep within the bows that lather
Lyudmila's armpit, taxis and controls her
Until they stand foursquare beside my priest
And wait erect to start their human feast.

We're nearly done here. I just can't narrate
And sermonise in tandem. I'm recording,
Don't worry. It won't be an anguished wait.
I won't list all the carriages I'm boarding
Across the eurozone's benighted borders.
We'll jump straight back. The muse has given orders.

But one last lingering new camera angle,
Before the great director in the sky
Calls "cut!" and drops her silken blind to strangle
The light from every squinting bloodshot eye.
The kind of shot that pulls away to spare us
From images that might be ripe to scare us:

The Geckocam™ – ensconced within the cope
Inside the barn's cracked rim of serried brick –
Provides this panned-out, more expansive scope:
The village elm, a knobbled candlestick,
Casts down a knuckled shade across the players
Who shuffle tight like thirsting vampire slayers

And, though more rough and buffeted than buff,
Possess an air of menacing bloodthirst
That strums capillaries and pricks their scruff
Communally. Poor Sissy fears the worst.
He sees their eyeballs' infra-red dilating
And loses all last thoughts of celebrating.

Oh hammock, how I missed you! Your kind netting
That softens to accommodate my molecules!
My sling of comfort, wherein, after jetting
Or trundling, I lay down my weathered follicles!
I stretch myself out showered, supine, restful,
But in your arms my brain's already zestful!

My journey back I shall not speak too much of.
The muse wants brevity, not histrionics. ♪
But Warsaw was a blast again: a clutch of
My favourite clubs and friends; live electronics
In Praga's *Klub Bo Na Na*; Lech and Jan
Were on top form and spread their warm élan.

♪ On forty-nine sleek yards of golden chrome
  In Dresden (a day off, to ride the trams)
  I wended past the Frauenkirche dome,
  A scratched baroque balloon (one of the scams
  Of post-war *trompe l'oeil*), then looped round the Zwinger's
  Rococo shape and jobbing opera singers.

St Pancras greeted me. Its myriad chains,
Paul, Costa, The West Cornwall Pasty Co.
(Faux favourite of pink toffs with shit for brains)
Spat their indentikit untempting glow.
Beneath the arcing firmament of glass.
Now west of Europe, grub is second class.

Now for a dark confession: I was tired,
The only mitigation for what followed.
My Brompton was in Penge to be re-tyred
By no-fee Buddhist velophiles. I swallowed
All shame, released a *Boris bike* and rode
In self-disgust to where my barge was stowed.

The lights beneath the Vauxhall smog still glistened
In affluent reflection on the moorings
Of bijoux maison-barges. If one listened
With shot glass to their glossy hulls, outpourings
Of bitter pinots noirs and lustless cheer
Would bubble out and fondle with your ear...

Köln Hauptbahnhof was still in shape, still bursting
With jolly blaggers happily *glim lurking*
("Professing tales of loss by fire") and thirsting
For kölsch-fund coins; the Dom's Hail Bell still jerking
From side to side at every punctual *stunde*
In peals of civilising Saxon thunder.

Bruxelles Midi was as it ever is:
The indoor pigeon muck, the shrill refrain
Of tinny and trilingual tannoy-fizz
Announcing yet another waylaid train,
The self-propelled piano (Chopin, Liszt),
The air all waffle-greased and coffee-kissed.

But neighbours are no interest to our story,
Especially these riparian co-bobbers.
Built of the dullest chromosomes, they bore me
To tears. Let's leave them be. I cannot sob as
The climax of our wild adventure flies
Towards us like an anvil from the skies.

Beneath the river's film a squad of pike
Encircles the municipal toy vélo.
(I felt compelled to kill. My own dear bike
Will not forgive my trip on this bordello
Of tarty saddle. Her slim spokes will sense
My shame when I next mount her, cowed and tense.)

My bags unpacked and laundry gently soaking,
My trunk and guilt soap-purged of grime and sin,
My laptops charged, their frantic hard-drives croaking
Like microcosmic Basho toads within,
The tide beneath me surges to the east,
Its waters charged with oriental yeast.

My outfit? I thought this was clear: I'm nude.
(The barge is well-equipped with radiation.)
The moon beams from behind a drifting brood
Of watchful cumulus. A grey striation
Of oil and Tilbury-bound *spumante* stipples
The river-skin in slow spasmodic ripples.

The bridges pass above my lone flotilla:
First Vauxhall's scratched red arc, the diabolic
Two-tone of Lambeth, Westminster's green Scylla,
Then Hungerford's railroad of chugging colic.
At Waterloo I pause to take in chatter
On post theatrical and filmic matter:

(Apparently a *smashing* young Othello
Outdoes the Kurosawa retrospective
And Britten's Rostropovich Suites for Cello
Are too indulgent, Deller lacks perspective
In searching for the not-so-long-lost Bez...
And in the bar: "avoid the corked Jerez").

Then on: Blackfriars road bridge, then the rail one –
Now freed of dusty skins of keen construction
(A station on a bridge!) though, quick, I sail on
To Southwark, pulled on by an eastbound suction,
I pass the Globe where *out vile spot wherefore*
Art thou dear Friends that I did love the Moor

I would not be or not to be glissandos
Across the waters. London Bridge then rears
Its back-lit spine. My vessel ritardandos
Between the pinkish pinions, landing gears
Engage, the Geckopilot™ trims the power
And glides us to a cove beside the Tower.

Upon my stream I watch glossed Shoreditch quiffs
And Debbie Harry bleach-jobs strut and preen
Along a boho queue like docking skiffs
Outside their harbour – a converted skein
Of decommissioned nailbars, Halal diners
And dead boutiques that stocked deceased designers.

A "gallery space" south of Dalston Junction
(Now squatted by a quod of Nathan Barleys)
The unit's new cognomen "Four Man Function"
Hosts vernissages, glitch-hop nights, group parlays
On *conscious apps for 99percenting*
And *how to live without the chains of renting*.

Dyspeptic slots from anguished open-mic'ers
Tell confreres of their battles with the Man
And Powerpoint displays by urban hikers
Sing psychogeographic flights of Flân
Through carparks, disused tube-shafts, buried rivers,
While bootlegged Polish lager tickles livers.

And here, for one night only, an artista
Known uninominally like Adele,
Pelé or Maradona, as "The Sister"
Has set up a unique display: *The Well
Of Distant Pain*. A grainy eight-foot screen
And wall of cuttings we've already seen:

The travelcards, the vials of flat Bordeaux,
The pinch of skunk, the printed *billets-douxs*
Exchanged between a virtual Belle and Beau,
The pen-and-inks besmirched in fishy glue,
The dating portal screen-shots, Neno Brown
A mask of bile beneath his bloody crown.

Beth cradles Neno's pixels in her tank top's
Stuffed Lycra cauliflower. A frozen tear
Drops vainly on his cheek. A clotted bank stops
Its salted path to where his dextral ear
Once jutted like a handle from his face's
Proud goblet then dissolves in grief-filled stasis.

The ghastly bunker where she found him choking
In his own sanguinary overflow
Now fills with yellow plumes. The Troika, smoking
Three fat Padrons, approach. Their shadows grow
Like Sendak beasts beneath the dim fluorescence
Of naked bulbs. Beth curls in acquiescence.

They do that clichéd gangster thing, imploring
"Don't worry lady, everything is fine,"
In tones so dread and wildly unassuring
That Beth's as frozen as a Tomski pine.
"Our *new* boss"; "Come, we have a car"; "Don't whelp,
There's no need"; "He'd just *love* to meet"; "He'll help."

So Neno's corpse is left to defragment
Beneath a moody Second London graphic
("GAME OVER Mr Brown. Your credit's spent")
The troika and their doll plough through the traffic,
Down tunnels digital, through neon fog as
A bloodshot morning floods with tiny joggers.

They pull up in a ball of purple dustiness
At Foksal Heights, just as pale double suns
Criss-cross above in pixelated rustiness.
Beth simpers to the lift (a pair of guns
Encourage her, poked gently in her spleen)
And does as bade by Jeb ("press 17").

The rooftop garden city is patrolled
By sanguine guards in Bloods and Cripps chromatics.
Their colours here are mere aesthetics, hold
No symbolistic threat of automatics
And sawn-off Colts erupting through South-Central.
In fact, they're all clean-lipped and reverential:

"Could I entreat you possibly dear Homie
To loan me briefly if you would your hoe?
The rhododendron bed's a little loamy
And needs a shuffle." "Sure, Dogg! Here you go.
Perhaps you'd also like to bust a cap on
Your lustrous pate? These suns can really sap one."

"Indeed I would. How kind. Mine gives me itches.
That's why I rock the bald look, but you're right.
It's wise to shade the brain. How are your bitches?"
"Oh, cool." "And all the puppies?" "Keeping tight."
"And pussy action? Doing well?" "I'm smitten!
I've just rehomed a lovely Persian kitten!"

But why so blissed, these Rufios in bandanas?
Wherefore their usual restless misanthropia?
The trick is in the weed. Their *Pollianas*
Are laced with such a hazy pharmacopoeia
That now they're more East Cornwall than East Compton.
The calming kingpin pusher Mr Brompton,

His slippered feet upon a *żubr*-hide pouffe,
Surveys things from behind thatched wormwood fences;
Burnt sugar skylights glaze his office roof;
His workplace hums-organic in all senses –
With mohawked guard-wasps on their zig-zig beats
And gossiping bilingual parakeets.

Beth enters, shuffling slow and trepidacious,
And stops before Herr Brompton's smiling shape.
"Dear Bethany, your fear would be vexatious,
If I were not so patient. No escape
Is possible, resistance would be awful...
And might compel my friends to get unlawful."

She gulps and summons up some latent spunk,
"What did you do to Neno? Let me go!"
"You're either immemorious or drunk,
What happened to your friend we both well know.
A truly tragic accident. But life,
They say, goes on..." "My *friend*, what? I'm his wife!"

"Ah, sweetheart, here I should perhaps explain:
Don't use the sentimental present tense
When speaking of that Brown. I feel your pain,
Of course, but loss brings with it recompense.
I've made arrangements." "What?" "No need for pining.
You're my wife now. A perfect silver lining."

Beth turns a silent shade of very still
(Externally. Within, her feisty heart
Is overcharged with pained systolic chill).
"Umm, I don't think..." "I think you do. Let's start
By shuffling off those silly pointy shoes".
Beth crumples, bends. There's nothing left to lose.

Let's drift away. This Second Earthy chapter
Is closing as Herr Brompton purrs delight
At Bethany's undressing toes. His capture
Inspires a flood of florid dynamite
To coruscate across the second sky
And splinter pyrotechnically on high.

For every winner here there is a loser.
So where is Sissy? Back ensconced in mum?
Well, yes. It took a while. Their railroad cruiser
Propelled them back to London's southern scum
Without the pit-stop playtimes I partook of.
They both craved, quickly, streets they knew the look of.

The trauma of the ceremony lingered
And skulked within their raw and pulsing brains.
Their medullae and cerebellums fingered
By wheedling flashbacks, throbbed as they changed trains
And blighted provenders of stodge and lipid
For platform fare pre-toasted and insipid.

The whole way home the new groom rode externally.
In mutual shock, the couple barely spoke.
Once back in Dulwich calm (its sempiternally
Suburban drift of prams and tandoor smoke)
It took a day or two for eyes to meet
And mum to grant her boy his loved retreat.

Eventually, obliquely, the word wife
Was mentioned. "It's a pity. Her tradition.
This 'buffer week' before full married life."
"Yes, heartsweet. Odd. Perhaps, though, this remission
Will turn up on the longer terms more wise...
Why not stock-take and then reunionise?"

All proto-nuptial joy came to desert her.
She spoke this way from simple mother's instinct.
A filioectomy would disconcert her
(In painful literal terms) but, too, the slim tinct
Of freedom that appealed re his promotion
To nest-flown *man* seemed like a faded notion.

It spread, this cloudy PTSD numbness,
To most domestic functions. She refrained from
All wardrobe change and fouled one paisley sundress
Repeatedly with varied biles that drained from
Her porous epidermis, whether resting
Or exercising (i.e., when ingesting).

No, this inertia didn't spread to feeding.
In fact increased consumption as displacement
Activity broke records: each gut needing
An exponential spadeful as the days went
Morosely by: son's sleep-encrusted thorn
Withdrawing to the cake tin every dawn...

On hairless ham hock feet he'd scuttle bedward
With piles of Battenberg and *pains de buerres*
To mum, now pilloried against the headboard,
Her frame played like a harp by gastric purrs.
The duo gorged on, daily escalating
Their intake in a whirr of masticating.

A bloated week of nine square meals a day
(In bed or in the bath or on the throne,
With added snack breaks) passed. The rapid play
Of winter suns arced; rounded shadows, thrown
On eggshell walls rose, fell. Then this arrived:
Dear Hello Husband! Hoping you are thrived!

I make return to London on next night!
How many times I miss you with whole heart!
Mine own exploding soon (as dynamite!)
For see you and begin our second start!
I will not writing excess on this junction!
Let's meet us on one gallery: Four Man Function!

He almost choked. His bacon Rogan Josh
Swelled nervous in his pharynx's stuffed tunnel.
His stomach felt the palpitating cosh
Of heavy metal butterflies, the funnel
Of fudge between his colon's leaden pool
And sphincter's flapping eye began to drool.

But things had gone too far for any bailout.
It's not as if a kindly central bank
Could offer a reprieve. No desperate mailout
By charitable trusts could fund a tank
To drive through his gaunt army of disquiet
And quell his every cell's internal riot.

So Sissy duly tapped off a reply:
Yes, love to see you then. It should be fab.
The cold ensuing day went thus: wash, dry,
Eat (less than usual, one five-pound kebab,
One Nandos, one terrine of cheezy fries),
Pluck, shave, exfoliate, rinse, moisturise.

Mum fetched and pressed a Daz-doused smorgasbord
Of favourite shirts (a floral YSL,
A cornflower Ralph, a crimson microcord
Versace...) Sissy turned towards his gel
And lubed in product every fraying follicle
To form a coxcomb maladroit and conical.

Then time to leave. Two hours were more than ample
To get to Dalston. FMF's cheap site
Read "Doors 9:30(ish)". He clicked <<play sample
For preview slides of what's on show tonight>>.
I gulped *(Oh dear. This wrecks it)* then remembered
(What blissed recall!) I'd left the links dismembered...

And now, wings stilled, our eye goes telescopic
And squints to score the vernissage's heroine.
Her mien is calm, her aura's spectroscopic
And flushes when the bouncers let her fellow in.
You'd think that now she'd hide or wildly greet him.
Both cases wrong. She'll work the room. Then meet him

First worm-wise, through chicanes of vacant plinths,
She sashays, smiling, waving, shaking hands,
Then, as the music rises (stabbing synths
And sampled strains of Balkan marching bands)
She steps into a dance and pirouettes
Towards the drinks and canapé cuvettes.

The venue's corrugated skin is dripping
With garlands of entangled fairy lamps
As cool kids flow in steadily. Boys sipping
From beakers of vermouth check out young vamps
In twelve-hole DMs; stockinged flapper types
Peruse the next-gen Teds in retro stripes.

Our artiste pauses by the cocktails, smirking,
And watches all these bright young things assembling.
She quaffs a snowball, swallows whole a gherkin,
Then spots him, propping up a corner, trembling,
His head one minute static, ashen, cowed
Then scanning fearfully across the crowd.

"Hi there, I'm Magda. Thanks for stopping by.
The installation kicks off bang on ten.
How did you hear about the show? But, why
How rude of me! What is *your* name?" "Well... Ben,
My friend... told me. I'm Sissy." Still his eyes
Pan round in blinded hope past her disguise.

But he can't see her. Where is his Lyudmila?
She said that she would be here! Oh, despair
Now blooms like an impassioned granadilla
Within his tightened chest. Her flaming hair?
Her porcelain complexion? They've deserted him.
But Magda's face has somehow disconcerted him.

She seems familiar. But then perhaps
He simply seeing Lyuda's absent shape
In everyone and thing: a glass of schnapps,
A dusty ball of crumpled Sellotape,
The cracks within the floor, the curlicues
Of pungent steam, the flickering tattoos.

They part as quickly as they came together.
She presses more enamoured cheeks and palms.
He gazes from behind his brows' tense leather
Until he's offered patient social alms:
Wassily's empathetic eyes perceive him
As lost. He sidles over to relieve him.

(He leaves drunk Iza caught in wild dispute of
Her ratio of gin to Slimline tonic.
She doesn't even see her husband shoot off
Across the room, such is her histrionic
Insistence that a Bombay mix encumbers
The barman to provision *diced* cucumbers.)

They chat, distractedly on Sissy's part,
Intense on Wassily's, until they strike
A mutual chord that twangs each other's heart:
"Last week (though, shh, this isn't open mic)
I made a family trip to west Ukraine."
"Oh... really?" Sissy focusses. "By train?"

"How did you know?" "Just guessed." "The only way
If you are burdened by a bulky freight.
The cut-throat airlines live to make you pay
With monstrous add-on fees for excess weight.
But have you ever been there?" "Been to where?"
"The eastern fringe of Europe's fraying hair."

"The way you sensed my trip was made on rails,
I thought, perhaps...?" "Um... no... I think I read about
A journey to those parts, that's all." He flails
His cornflower arms and *Shock Waves*-crested head about
(This happens with a lie. He must defend it
With *Gestus*). "Well you should. I recommend it."

Our hero's twitching trunk says "if you say so"
And soon reverts to searching for his wife.
The crowd has crammed the space like humid Play-doh
And... tick-tock: time's unsubtle clockwork knife
Has struck on ten. Like dying *Lampyrini*
The lights dim. Magda gulps a stiff Bellini.

The bodies push yet tighter, sweat commingles
With *Pomegranate Noir* and *Violet Blonde*
And suddenly a piercing bell blast tingles
Through each tympanic membrane's tender bond.
The screen wakes up and floods the deafened hall.
A Malevichesque square fills one white wall.

As if it were a sheet of silver paper
Emerging from a dark room's magic wells
An image coalesces through the vapour
Of spinning, deep vermillion asphodels.
Their revolutions grow intenser, petals
Fly off, transmogrify, a profile settles:

Lyudmilla's page on Slavic Beauties glowers
Above the craning necks. Her declaration
"I loving active rest and smell from flowers"
Inspires a wave of light anticipation
In all but one of the attendant throng.
For Sissy this is going more than wrong.

At least, an optimist could say, he's found her.
There's no more need to scour the gallery.
(That optimist would be a gleeful bounder
Or else an idiot.) To fight? To flee?
These are the classic paths that can be chosen
At times like these. Unless, of course, you're frozen.

So Sissy does his best to disappear
Into the ground and prays he sublimates
To join the laughing gaseous atmosphere.
The portrait on the screen recalibrates.
Satsuma locks turn brown, eyes bulge and blacken,
The nose swells and retroussés, nostrils slacken.

BEN BOREK

Now Sissy stares down at himself. "O Jesus!
Please help me!" he breathes out as he stares back.
He feels as if a monstrous swarm of tweezers
Have hit him in a many-mouthed attack
And clasped all of his fraying nerve receptors
Then stabbed each one with tiny hateful sceptres.

Live audio from Sissy's inner ear:
I should have stayed with mum and just pretended
This wasn't happening. Why am I here?
The last few weeks were dreams. This should have ended
Once we got back. Perhaps it's still a dream?
Where is Lydumilla? God, I want to scream!

The answer to his final question hits
Immediately like a slap. On screen
It's All Bar One, and there Lyudmilla sits.
Her cold Tatanka throbs a livid green
Between her patient palms. The *maître d'*
(Your handsome poet) looks on attentively

As Sissy now emerges, overheating
And panting, like a man-size, well-shaved pug.
"You shall be Sissy! So glad we can meeting!"
Resounds through Four Man Function's bated fug.
Some music fills the hall – the Liszt sonata –
As we all watch the couple choose their starter.

We know what happens next, we saw it live,
So as they eat and Sissy's fabulation
Grows wilder with each sip of drink, let's skive
Backstage, where one last costume transformation
Sees Magda fling off paint-stained Shoreditch frocking
And squeeze into Lyudmilla's body stocking.

"So far, so good?" "Indeed. So good, so far!
You're doing great. We're very nearly there."
"My Bow beautician's late (can't find his car).
"Please pass that wig." I toss across her hair.
"And now those eyelashes. And now that knife."
"That *what*?" "Relax! Remember, I'm his *wife*..."

She preps her features in a greasy compact,
Applies a grin of Hollywood cerise,
Then bastes her shoulders, nape and dimpled entr'acte
Between her hoisted breasts in sparkling grease.
"Superb. My dear! You've shifted paradigm!"
"You'd best get back out front. It's nearly time."

Upon the screen the action has progressed.
The pair are now in Vauxhall. Underground.
Our hero, comprehensively undressed,
Excretes a pitifully tiny sound.
Lyudmilla stands above him, wreathed in strapping,
And sings at him in tones like thunder clapping.

The content of this lyric malefaction
Is not discernible to human ears,
But to its dread vibration one reaction
Is certain: now the floorboards flood with tears.
A slick of liquid tentacles have slid
From underneath his heap like maudlin squid.

She bends on squeaking polyvinyl knees
And strokes the spittle from his trembling chin
Then reaches to her left. A squat valise
Clicks open at her splendid feet. Within
A villainous array of apparatus
Awaits her happy fingers of afflatus:

Lyudmilla slows her dirge as she unpacks
Pink rubber bands, syringes, balls of chain,
An adult nappy, spanner, handcuffs, wax,
Black sandpaper, a length of flex, a cane
Of rusted tin and seven frosted bottles –
Their contents: squirming newts and axolotls.

The screen goes black. The audience all shuffle
Excitedly within their modish footwear.
As speakers stream a slow metallic scuffle
They strain to work out what is being put where
When something whelps or scrapes or clicks or cries,
But one or two can't bear to visualise.

How long this blind show lasts is hard to gauge.
For me, it passes like a beam of light
Across a titan's retina. An age
Of sorrow though, an endless sickened night,
Of this doom-laden black *musique concrete*
Has rendered Sissy now a statuette.

Around him giggles swell. The gathered throng
Becomes one raucous blanket of hilarity.
The piped percussion cuts. A violent gong
Announces the return of visual clarity.
The spotlit screen's white skin begins to crest
And bulge... and then acquires a sharpened breast.

Lyudmila's blade then slashes neatly through.
She cuts a crucifix of flapping cloth
And pokes out an absurdly high-heeled shoe.
With one crazed bound (half war-wild Ostrogoth,
Half catwalk flouncing glam-bot) she appears,
A grin slung deep and loose between her ears.

"Dear Hello Sissy! I am came for you!"
She trills into the silent throbbing airspace.
The gods of techno take this as their cue
And music floods the hall. A groan of snare, bass
And daubs of sampled Vauxhall machination
Accompany this subsequent oration:

"I am for you one woman in the life!
With many dancing how I make return!
We be with us together man and wife!"
And suddenly a dozen screens all burn
To crackling grainy life about the hall
With celluloid of last week's wedding ball.

Here's Pan Demenchonok's bald salutation;
The Popov's lacing mother like a goose;
Nadezdha Filipovna's application
Of pre-nup love, here's Uncle Vlad's caboose
Of donkey meat and vodka for the feast;
Lyudmila on the aisle; your gorgeous priest...

Our hero sees this all through fingers splayed
Across his disbelieving slitted eyes.
The sight of mother on the screen has made
Denial all the harder. Still he tries:
If I just breathe in deep and count to ten,
I'll blink then be back home in mum again...

Lyudmila's poetry soon pops that bubble,
Her fingers gouge that desperate ball of hope
With scarlet in-fills, existential rubble
Rains down in Sissy's skull. *One holy rope*
Was made like dart of god and shooted straight
From London to mine village, through mine gate

It made most magic path, across mine scullery,
Around old samovar, past three-leg table
And sleepy goat! With rainbow happy colour we
Together now because one special cable
Make in my laptop messages your hand
Have wrote with love from distance Dulwich land!

Now union can happy be complete!
Mine leg and arm and bosom be for sharing!
On unity us live in Vauxhall street
With cat or dog or baby, I not caring!
So came to me for dance, for celebrate,
Mine darling husband, came! Now I await!

Throughout all this she spins her louche cotillion
To Sissy in his quaking corner hideout.
Her Poundland bangles chime a cheap carillon
Of plastic against tin, her boot heels slide out
Beneath, two compass needles on a map
Chop-chopping to an ever closer trap.

The air by now is close and fraught with laughter,
Some genuine, from beer-lined throats and guts,
Some bashful and contrived, a half beat after
The punchline's cold salacious épée cuts.
For Sissy though, the motive for the rapture
Means nothing. It still presages his capture.

One final whirligig of limbs. Lyudmila
Now stands before her husband. Fragrant sweat
Infuses her environs. A cedilla
Of *Eau de Donetsk* trickles down the net
That stretches tight as cling film round her bust
Then drops to earth and spits up crackling dust.

The chamber blackens once again. The walls
Bleed moisture and more scuffling from the speakers.
Then silence. Sissy's inward caterwauls
Seep out as tiny, soundless bleats as meek as
A toothless stillborn lamb's. And then a kiss
As welcome as a dose of syphilis:

A spotlight hits the couple, now connected
In what we'll call an improvised French oral.
Lyudmila, much more Gallic, lips injected
With gleeful force, her tongue robust and chloral,
Is quite the osculating muscle-dancer
And won't take Sissy's closure as no answer.

And now a hoarse tsunami of applause:
"O god, like, wow! That was just, like, so cool!"
"They're really man and wife?" "No way!" "Of course!"
"You saw the videos!" "God, what a fool!"
"She plucked him like an instrument!" "She chewed him
Up and spat him out!" "She really screwed him!"

"And now she is again... I don't believe it..."
"She's pulling off his shirt, she's on his flies...
For Wassily this show's too much. "Let's leave it,"
He says to drunken Iza, "Shield your eyes."
She won't, of course, until he spins and drags her
Towards the door. "Remember, that is *Magda*!"

Outside they meet the night air's icy flue
And hail a cab for distant Cricklewood.
Farewell dear Wassily! Iza, adieu!
A midnight game of tipsy slap and tickle should
Becalm the pair of you. I wish you luck.
Remember it's more fun to love than ruck!

But back within – the death throes of the floor show.
Its coda is unravelling inside:
Upon the sawdust Sissy's naked pores flow
With grease beneath his undulating bride.
There's quite a noise, but now it's hard to say
If it's live grunting vox or more PA.

A hundred geckos (hand cut, silver foil)
Now flutter from the rafters. UV lighting.
A hissing from the walls: dry ice; a coil
Slides serpentine like looped left-handed writing
Across the empty screen and then expands
To wrap our duo in thick fumacious hands.

The lights go down conclusively. The crowd
Release a deep collective breath. Canned hip hop
And Aphex Twin escorts them out. Heads bowed,
Eyes watery, they file towards the chip shop
On Abbot Street for post-artistic greasiness
And further gin to tonic their uneasiness.

What's left upon the floor: a ball of smoke
Like cloudy bindweed wrestling its own tendrils.
My Geckocams™ all pan away and choke.
Last ditherers book cab rides to The End. Frills
And scraps of moribund costume now litter
The vacant parquet, soaked in lime and bitter.

I'll wrap things up now, literally, by sheathing
Our couple in a thick angora rug.
Beneath, Sissy is labouring his breathing
(His respiration like a sickened pug
Consumed by an invidious bereavement),
While Magda giggles softly with achievement.

And now a quick retreat. I load my pannier
With installation: film, clothes, sheets, projectors;
And pedal back to where my own Britannia
Waits lulled upon the neap tide's gleaming vectors.
The streets stream in a post-pub anaphylaxis
Of topless teenage men and belching taxis.

A lecherous half moon squints down to earth –
Its iris wulfenite, its lid bubonic –
And casts an ochre film across the turf:
The Tower of London's turrets, catatonic
And limpid are inverted in the Thames,
To glimmer round my barge's frothing hems.

So here we are. The end of time. The climax
(Or post-climactic scene). I'm in my snug
And sip a frozen Bols. Port side: the iMax
At Waterloo (that glowing whale-size slug)
Slips soundlessly behind our graceful barque
And quickly evanesces in the dark;

The ring of mutant pterodactyl eggs
In incubation round their Ferris wheel
Soon fade away as phosphorescent dregs
Reflecting in the slipstream of our keel;
The river bends beneath us; mallards hide
In hollow moss-daubed buoys on starboard side.

Behind us arch the stolid spines of bridges
Like cankerous grey digits round a chord
Of terraqueous yarn. Night haemorrhages
And bleary rays besmear the concrete sward.
Past Westminster I cut the keen propeller
And let us drift beneath dawn's rose umbrella.

Tradescantia's sweetly botryose aroma
Flits through the cabin as we pass the garden
At Lambeth Palace. I am both your Homer
And Ulysses as Vauxhall's features harden
And focus (they're my Ithaca). We're home.
The Geckopilot™ guides us through the foam.

And lo! The gaudy hum of Vauxhall Cross:
The same Ghanaian cleaners finish night shifts,
The same three languid tracksuits jog across
The traffic island as the amber light shifts
To bloodshot red, the same sad dog and master
Still cruise the bridge like animated plaster.

I tie my silk kimono's dangling sash
And slip my deck shoes on. A shape awaits
Upon the northern shore. Soft wavelets plash
Against her perfect feet. The muse dictates
That things should finish now. So, Magda, catch
This landing rope I lovingly dispatch.

ACKNOWLEDGEMENTS

Thanks first and foremost to Nathan Hamilton, who has helped in many, many ways with the various versions and shapes, chops and changes, and has been with me as the goals went in. Thanks also to others who have seen parts of the book at different stages and encouraged, criticised, prodded: Edmund Hardy, Natalia Janota, Alistair Noon, James Wilkes, Caroline Rohde-Nielsen, Alex Coxen.

The writing of this book was greatly assisted by the Society of Authors' with an Arthur Welton Award from their Authors' Foundation (www.societyofauthors.org/Grants/Grants-for-works-in-progress).

An earlier version of the Dom Tańczący section first appeared online at Intercapillary Space (2012).

Sissy
By Ben Borek

First published in this edition by Boiler House Press, 2019
Part of UEA Publishing Project
Copyright © Ben Borek, 2019

Design and typesetting by Emily Benton Book Design
Typeset in Arnhem Pro
Printed by Tallinn Book Printers
Distributed by NBN International

ISBN 978-1-911343-57-8